S268 Physical Resources and Environment
Science: a second level course

BLOCK

METALS 1

ORE DEPOSITS

Prepared for the Course Team by Peter Webb

S268 Physical Resources and Environment

Course Team

Dave Williams (Course Chair)
Andrew Bell
Geoff Brown
Steve Drury
Chris Hawkesworth
Ian Nuttall (Editor)
Janice Robertson (Editor)
Peter Sheldon
Sandy Smith
Peter Webb
Chris Wilson
John Wright
Annemarie Hedges (Course Manager)
Charlie Bendall (Course Coordinator)

Production

Jane Sheppard (Graphic Designer)
Steve Best (Graphic Artist)
David Jackson (Series Producer, BBC)
Nicholas Watson (BBC Producer)
John Greenwood (Liaison Librarian)
Eira Parker (Course Secretary)
Marilyn Leggett (Secretary)
Lynn Tilbury (Secretary)

Course assessor

Professor Peter W. Scott, Camborne School of Mines.

Dedication

Professor Geoff Brown was a member of the Course Team when he was killed on the Galeras Volcano, Colombia, in January 1993. The Course Team dedicates S268 to his memory.

Acknowledgements

The Course Team gratefully acknowledges the contributions of members of the S238 course team (S238 *The Earth's Physical Resources*, 1984).

The Course Team also wishes to thank Sheila Dellow for careful reading of early drafts of the course material.

The Open University, Walton Hall, Milton Keynes MK7 6AA.

First published 1995. Reprinted with corrections 1999. Reprinted 2003.

Edited, designed and typeset by The Open University.

Printed in the United Kingdom by Henry Ling Limited, at the Dorset Press, Dorchester, DT1 1HD.

ISBN 0 7492 5150 6

This text forms part of an Open University second level course. If you would like a copy of *Studying with the Open University*, please write to the Central Enquiry Service, PO Box 200, The Open University, Walton Hall, Milton Keynes, MK7 6YZ. If you have not already enrolled on the course and would like to buy this or other Open University material, please write to Open University Educational Enterprises Ltd, 12 Cofferidge Close, Stony Stratford, Milton Keynes, MK11 1BY, United Kingdom.

Edition 1.3

S268block5part1i1.3

CONTENTS

1 INTRODUCTION TO METALS AND ORE DEPOSITS

Without metals, the modern world we live in would not exist, at least, not in the form that we know it. When we look around us, however, it may not be immediately obvious how important metals are, and how much we depend on them. We may see a few objects made of metals, and examples of their *direct use*, but we are more likely to notice objects made of concrete, wood, cloth and plastics — just some of the familiar non-metallic materials that form part of everyday life in the 1990s. But how are they produced? First, the raw materials have to be obtained: by harvesting from plants or extraction from the ground; then processed, often in stages, by industry to convert them into useful products; and at each stage, transportation is necessary, both to supply raw materials and deliver finished products. In *all* these activities, *metals are essential*: they are required for machinery, in building construction, for power supply, and in transport (see Figure 1). So, although many of the materials we use are not made of metal, metals are required for their manufacture, and they represent an *indirect use* of metals. In addition there are many essential human activities, such as food production, that could not be undertaken efficiently without metals. On reflection, could you imagine our industrialized world *without* metals?

The importance of metals is probably greater today than ever before, although their value has been appreciated by humans for at least 9 000 years. The first usage involved metals that occur naturally, if uncommonly, on the land surface, such as nuggets of native copper and gold that could be beaten into useful shapes. Since that time there has been a slow discovery — though probably by accident at first — of techniques involving fire and charcoal that could convert minerals rich in lead, copper, zinc and tin into a metallic state.

Figure 1 The importance of metals in the modern world; their indirect uses are not always obvious. (a) A large hole would be difficult to dig without an excavator; (b) bulk shipment of freight would be difficult without ships or trains; (c) manufacturing of all kinds would be difficult without machines; and (d) without turbines and power lines, how could we generate and transmit power in the quantities demanded today?

(a)

(b)

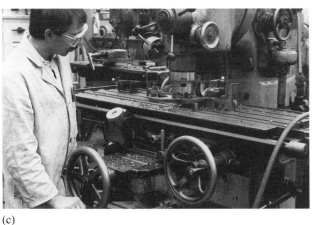

(c)

(d)

Lead beads are known from 8 000 years ago, well before the first evidence of copper smelting and mining of the copper carbonate minerals, malachite and azurite, in the Balkans about 6 500 years ago. Copper working later became more extensive in central Europe, and led to the discovery of bronze about 4 600 years ago by roasting tin and copper minerals with charcoal. Another 2 000 years elapsed before the production of iron became commonplace.

Early demand for metals was mainly for use as implements and ornaments, but with the development of stronger metals and the increase in supply, the use of metals in weapons became important. By the time the Romans came to Britain about 2 000 years ago, they were using iron and bronze for weapons, tools and farming implements; copper for jugs and ornaments; lead for pipes and coffins; tin, gold and silver for ornaments; and gold, silver, brass and bronze for coinage. It's only in the past 200 years or so, however, since the Industrial Revolution gained pace, that technological discoveries have led both to today's widespread and diverse uses of metals —summarized in Figure 2 — and to the dominance of iron, used mainly in the form of steel (Block 1, Section 1.3, and Video Band 1).

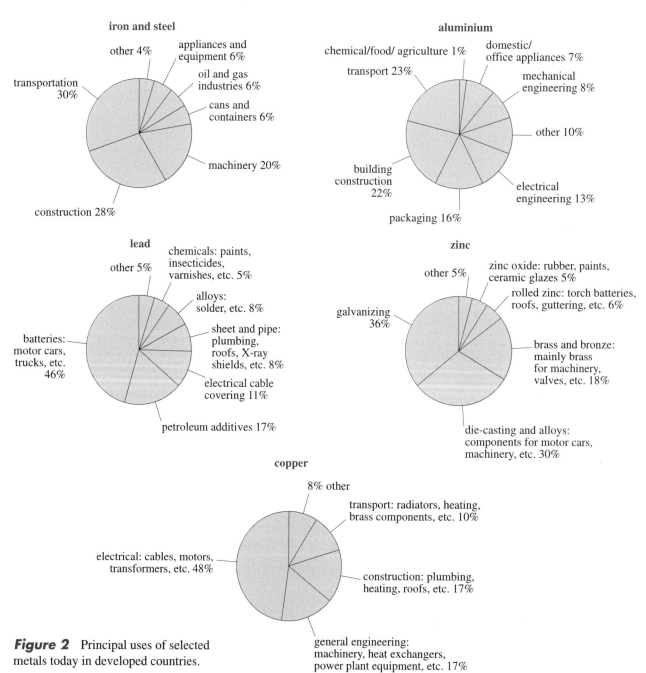

Figure 2 Principal uses of selected metals today in developed countries.

○ How much of today's metal use (described in Figure 2) is linked to the production of machinery, provision of transportation and power? These uses facilitate other activities, particularly the supply and production of other materials — the indirect use of metals noted earlier.

○ For iron and steel at least 56%, for copper at least 75%, for lead at least 74%, for zinc at least 48%, and for aluminium at least 44%.

This Block concentrates on metals as physical resources. It is in two parts: the first, *Metals 1 — Ore Deposits*, considers what makes natural deposits suitable for use as sources of metals, how and where these deposits were formed, and why some metals are more readily available than others. The second, *Metals 2 — Resource Exploitation*, examines how metal ores are found and extracted from the Earth, how the metal resources industry operates, how it affects the environment, and how changing technologies, consumer demands and economic factors have influenced the industry in the past and are likely to change it in the future in response to increasing environmental and conservation pressures.

First, let's consider what makes metals useful enough to be worth extracting from the Earth before considering the geological aspects of their availability.

1.1 Metals: their properties and uses

About 75% of the 94 naturally occurring chemical elements are metals. You may recall from Block 1 (Figure 41 and Audio Band 1) that *non-metals* occur at the top and the far right-hand side of the Periodic Table of elements; they include the noble gases and the halogens. A small number of elements are classified as metalloids, with properties intermediate between metals and non-metals. The rest of the Periodic Table consists of metals. Generally, the metallic character of elements *increases* down Groups (columns) and *decreases* across Periods (rows). For example, the Group that starts with the non-metal nitrogen at the top, ends with the metal, bismuth. At the left-hand side of the Periodic Table is the Group that arguably contains the most metallic of elements, the alkali metals, which are rarely used in their uncombined form because they are so reactive. They include sodium and potassium, which you have already encountered in the feldspar minerals, orthoclase ($KAlSi_3O_8$) and albite ($NaAlSi_3O_8$), and the evaporite minerals, halite ($NaCl$) and sylvite (KCl).

But how do we recognize a metal? Different people could easily come up with different definitions of a metal, depending on the properties with which they are most familiar. To most of us a **metal** is an opaque, shiny, often silvery or grey-coloured material that can be drawn into a wire and shaped by hammering, bending, or by melting and casting. To a physicist it may be a substance that can conduct both electricity and heat quite well, whereas a chemist might prefer to think of a metal as an element that forms positive ions (tends to lose electrons). An engineer might be more concerned with its strength, and a metallurgist might be more interested in its atomic structure and its response to heating and shaping.

What makes a metal different from a non-metal? Non-metallic substances include air, water, wood, bricks and plastics, as well as the non-metallic elements we have already noted. In general, non-metals are poor conductors of both heat and electricity; at room temperature some of them may be gases, others liquids, and yet others solids; and when solid they cannot usually be reshaped by bending or hammering. Non-metallic substances (especially plastics), however, have a wide range of properties, as indeed, do metals, so you can probably think of exceptions to most of these generalizations.

Let's take lead as an example, and see what its properties are. A good way to do this is to think when you last saw it used — and try to think *why* it was used. Perhaps it was as sealing strips along roofs (flashing), for its ability to be shaped by bending or hammering; its weight and strength, giving it stability; and its resistance to corrosion by the atmosphere and rainwater. Perhaps it was as terminals on a car battery, both for its ability to conduct electricity and its resistance to corrosion by battery acid. In fact, use in batteries amounts to almost half of all lead used (according to Figure 2).

○ Most of the properties we have described for lead are physical ones, but among them is one that is not physical but chemical. Which is it?

○ Chemical properties involve the **reactivity** of a substance — its ability to interact chemically with other substances. Lead is fairly unreactive in air, in water, and even in corrosive acidic solution. Its *resistance to corrosion* is a chemical property of special use and importance.

To give you a better idea of the wide range of properties that metals have, examine the list of metals and their properties in Table 1. Values are given for their melting temperatures in degrees Celsius (°C), and for their density, in tonnes per cubic metre ($t\,m^{-3}$), a unit which is not as unfriendly as it looks, because the numerical values are exactly the same as density quoted as grams per cubic centimetre ($g\,cm^{-3}$) or specific gravity. Clearly, lead is not the densest metal, although we think of it as very heavy; and, as it melts at relatively low temperatures, it can be easily cast into shape. Metals have a wide range of densities, from lithium, the lightest ($0.53\,t\,m^{-3}$), to osmium, the heaviest ($22.6\,t\,m^{-3}$). Apart from mercury, all metals are solids at room temperature.

The information in Table 1 about strength and types of conductivity is not given numerically, but in relative terms by a 'star' rating (* = low; **** = high). Electrical conductivity is a measure of the ease of transmitting electricity, and thermal conductivity, the ease of transmitting heat; values of both are quoted per unit cross-sectional area. Clearly, some metals are better conductors than others: copper is a good conductor of heat and electricity, but lead is a poor conductor of both (for a metal): in fact, copper is at least 10 times more efficient than lead at both forms of conduction.

Ease of corrosion is the only *chemical* property listed in Table 1, and is of great practical significance, but this property doesn't necessarily relate directly to the chemical reactivity of a metal. Some metals are reactive enough to combine with atmospheric oxygen to form an oxide layer that effectively protects the metal beneath. This is true, for example, of aluminium, on which a very thin oxide layer prevents further reaction, whereas for magnesium the layer of oxide gradually gets thicker with time, forming a powdery corrosion deposit. An extra 'property' given in Table 1 is price, which is often an important reason for choosing one metal in preference to another.

Table 1 Properties of selected metals

Metal	Symbol	Density[†]/ t m^{-3}	Melting temperature /°C	Tensile strength[‡]	Electrical conductivity[‡]	Thermal conductivity[‡]	Ease of atmospheric corrosion	Price[§] per tonne/$
aluminium	Al	2.7	659	**	***	***	oxide coating	1 270
chromium	Cr	7.2	1 890	****	**	**	very slow	5 950
copper	Cu	9.0	1 083	***	****	****	slow	2 290
gold	Au	19.3	1 063	**	***	****	does not corrode	11.1×10^6
iron	Fe	7.8	1 540	***	**	**	corrodes easily	205
lead	Pb	11.3	328	*	*	*	very slow	540
lithium	Li	0.53	180	*	**	**	oxide coating	—
magnesium	Mg	1.7	650	**	***	**	corrodes	3 310
mercury	Hg	13.6	−39	—	*	*	does not corrode	5 860
nickel	Ni	8.8	1 453	****	**	**	very slow	7 000
silver	Ag	10.5	961	***	****	****	tarnishes	127 000
tin	Sn	7.3	232	*	**	**	does not corrode	6 110
titanium	Ti	4.5	1 675	****	*	*	does not corrode	9 040
tungsten	W	19.3	3 410	****	**	***	does not corrode	7 310
zinc	Zn	7.1	420	*	**	**	very slow	1 240

†1 t m^{-3} = 1 Mg m^{-3} = 10^3 kg m^{-3} = 1 g cm^{-3}.

‡ Star rating: **** = high; * = low.

§ Prices are averages for 1992. The US dollar is the most widely used currency for metals pricing.

Question 1

Use the information in Table 1 to help you answer the following questions.

(a) Why is tungsten used as the filament in lightbulbs?

(b) Why is mercury used in glass thermometers?

(c) Why is titanium sometimes used in preference to aluminium for the construction of aircraft?

(d) Why are overhead electric power cables now made largely from aluminium rather than copper?

The importance of metals in engineering applications, such as construction, transportation and manufacturing, depends on several properties, including tensile strength, hardness and workability. *Tensile strength* — given in relative terms in Table 1 — is the ability to resist being pulled apart, which enables a bar, rod or beam to support a heavy load, so essential in the construction of buildings and bridges. *Hardness* is the ability to resist wear and pitting, which is important for weapons and tools to enable them to cut through or penetrate other materials. *Workability* can take on several forms, including *malleability*, the ability to be shaped through bending or hammering, and *ductility*, the ability to be drawn out to form a rod or wire. Both malleability and ductility involve ease of mechanical deformation without breaking. These properties are often well developed in metals; malleability is especially important when forming thin sheets such as gold leaf or pressing special shapes such as car body panels. Figure 3 shows some familiar examples of metal objects to illustrate properties typical of metals.

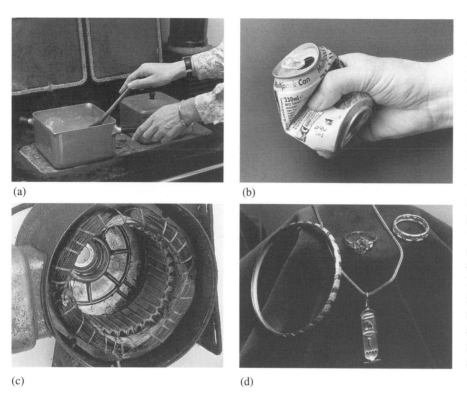

Figure 3 Objects made from common metals illustrate the usefulness of some of their properties. (a) A saucepan of aluminium is light, easily formed, resistant to corrosion, and transmits heat efficiently. (b) Aluminium is also used to make very thin cans, which are very light, corrosion resistant and watertight. (c) Copper windings at the heart of an electric motor are made of easily 'wound' wire; they transmit electricity efficiently, and can withstand considerable heating without burning out. (d) Gold jewellery is popular because it can be shaped to virtually any form and is unreactive, so it retains its bright, shiny appearance for a very long time.

(a) (b) (c) (d)

Table 2 outlines the importance of several properties of metals in a variety of applications. See how the usefulness of many metals depends on combinations of their properties by answering Question 2 and completing Table 2.

Question 2

(a) For metals used in tools and money *applications*, decide which of the properties given in Table 2 are most important and tick the relevant boxes.

(b) Using data from Table 1, write down in Table 2 which *suitable metal(s)* you would choose for use in tools, in fluid transport and in ornamentation.

(c) In which *applications* of Table 2 are (i) good thermal conductivity, and (ii) good electrical conductivity, important?

(d) From Table 2, which two *properties* are generally very desirable in most applications?

Table 2 Properties typically required of metals in common applications (in the final column the suitable metals suggested also take price into account)

Application (example)	Tensile strength	Workability	Hardness	Corrosion resistance	Appearance	Suitable metal
structures (bridges)	✓	✓		✓		Fe
transport (car chassis)	✓	✓		✓		Fe
tools (spanner)	☐	☐	☐	☐	☐	
electrical components (wire)	✓	✓		✓		Cu
cooling systems (car radiator)		✓		✓		Cu
containers (can)		✓		✓	✓	Al (Fe)
fluid transport (pipe)	✓	✓		✓		
fastenings (screws)	✓	✓		✓		Fe
weaponry (guns)	✓		✓	✓		Fe
ornamentation (jewellery)		✓		✓	✓	
money (coins)	☐	☐	☐	☐	☐	Cu, Ni

1.1.1 *Extending the uses of metals*

Although pure metals exhibit a wide range of properties, they have so many potential uses that finding ways of altering and enhancing their basic properties has long been of importance to the metallurgical industry. One of the first important metallurgical discoveries was that the presence of small amounts of arsenic in copper, provided naturally in certain types of copper ore, had the advantage of making copper harder. This was followed by the discovery of bronze, an even tougher metal, made from the ores of copper and tin. Such metallic mixtures are much like solid solutions in minerals, where a range of compositions are formed when one element substitutes for another. Metallic solid solutions of this kind are known as *alloys*. An example is the alloy duralumin, in which the main component, aluminium, confers lightness, but the addition of copper and magnesium increases the tensile strength many times. The addition of lithium—the lightest metal known—to aluminium alloys can make them significantly lighter, giving them a clear advantage for the construction of aircraft.

Table 3 gives the compositions of a number of common alloys, and shows how their properties are enhanced compared with pure metals. The metal that is most commonly used in alloyed form, in part because of its widespread availability and low price, but also for its inherent properties, is iron, which was the subject of Video Band 1: *The Great Iron and Steel Rollercoaster*. Iron is the basis of a vast range of steel alloys, which have been developed for their improved strength, hardness, high-temperature performance and corrosion resistance compared with other forms of iron (Table 3). Many metals, such as chromium, nickel, manganese, vanadium and tungsten, are of greater importance as components of steels than as metals in their own right.

Table 3 Table of alloys, their typical compositions and special properties

Alloy	Typical composition	Special properties
brass	Cu 70%; Zn 30%	harder than pure copper
bronze	Cu 90%; Sn 10%	harder than pure copper
duralumin	Al 94%; Cu 4%; Mg 2%	stronger than pure aluminium
solder	Sn 50%; Pb 50%	low melting temperature (203 °C)
mild steel	Fe 98.3%; Mn 1.5%; C 0.2%	stronger and more ductile than pure iron, but rusts
high-carbon steel	Fe 98.5%; C 1%; Mn 0.5%	harder than mild steel, but rusts
cast iron	Fe 97%; C 3%	hard but brittle; rust resistant
stainless steel	Fe 70%; Cr 20%; Ni 10%	harder than mild steel; does not rust
manganese steel	Fe 86%; Mn 13%; C 1%	very hard; resistant to abrasion
18-carat gold	Au 75%; Ag + Cu 25%	harder and cheaper than pure gold

Question 3

Use information from Tables 1 and 3 to answer the following questions.

(a) 'Silver' coins in the UK (e.g. 50p piece) are made of a cupro-nickel alloy composed of 75% copper and 25% nickel. Why have such alloys replaced silver metal for use in coins?

(b) Why is stainless steel used rather than mild steel to make knives?

(c) Why does solder contain tin *and* lead rather than only one or other metal?

(d) What type of steel might be most suitable for crushing rock?

Another way to extend the uses of metals is by coating a thin layer of one metal onto the surface of another. In this way, useful properties of the two metals can be combined. Thus, one of the main uses of zinc is still for coating steel (galvanizing, in Figure 2), which provides resistance to rusting without impairing the strength of the steel or increasing its price appreciably. Thin layers of chromium in chrome-plating and/or of aluminium for aluminizing often provide an attractive finish and corrosion resistance. Another reason for using a coating is to minimize cost. A coating of an expensive metal on a low-priced base, such as silver on nickel (electroplated cutlery) or gold on silver (silver gilt), is used to enhance appearance at reduced cost.

 Why are 'tin' cans not made entirely of pure tin?

Tin is very resistant to corrosion and is non-toxic, but it is relatively dense and expensive. Steel is stronger, more rigid, lighter and much cheaper than tin, but is subject to corrosion. 'Tin' cans are therefore made of tin plate — steel sheet coated with a very thin layer of tin (only $2\,\mu\text{m}$ thick). Aluminium cans are very much lighter than tin plate and also corrosion resistant, but aluminium is much more expensive per tonne than steel.

Recently, more and more materials that use both metals and non-metals in combination have been created. These materials are known as *composites*. Familiar examples include car tyres in which steel wire is embedded in rubber, and reinforced concrete, in which steel mesh increases the flexibility and the tensile strength of concrete slabs, pillars or beams.

Some metals have important uses in chemically combined form. For example, the hardness of tungsten carbide (WC) makes it suitable for use in cutting tools and rock-crushing equipment, and for the writing tips of high-quality ball-pens. In the early 1990s about one-sixth of lead (Figure 2) was used as tetraethyl-lead ($Pb(C_2H_5)_4$), the antiknock additive in high-octane petrol, but this fraction has decreased with the increased sale of unleaded petrol. An important use of molybdenum is in molybdenum disulphide (MoS_2), a high-temperature lubricant.

Having considered some of the more important properties of metals and the ways in which they are used, you should be able to tackle Activity 1.

Activity 1   Uses of metals in and around the home

(a) Look around your home and write down, if you can find them:
  (i)   five examples of the use of iron (in the form of cast iron, wrought iron or steel);
  (ii) four examples of the use of aluminium;
  (iii) three examples of the use of copper.

(b) From your examples, what do you think are the three most useful properties of each metal?

Give two cases in which the use of another of these metals as a substitute would be inappropriate, and explain why. Refer to Table 1 if necessary.

Note   As a rule, metallic iron can be readily identified with the help of a small magnet. In the home, materials that are attracted by a magnet are likely to contain iron, but a few other metals such as nickel can also be magnetic. Most steels, including most stainless steels, are magnetic with the exception of *austenitic steel*, which may contain just as much iron as other steels but is made in a special way that makes it non-magnetic.

Most aluminium objects used in the home appear silvery grey in colour (they may be bright and shiny or dull, as in aluminium wrapping foil); aluminium is non-magnetic and of relatively low density.

Copper has a distinctive appearance: it is usually smooth and a bright reddish brown. With time, fresh shiny surfaces become dulled, and when exposed to moist air for some years they form a green patina, or verdigris, a copper compound produced by corrosion of copper by atmospheric moisture.

1.1.2 Substitution and availability of metals

The demand for a metal ultimately depends on the properties that make it useful. If another substance, whether metal or not, has similar properties and can be used to do the same job, there is an opportunity for *substitution*. Various reasons for substitution were discussed extensively in Block 1 (Section 1.4). Probably the most common reason is an economic one — replacement by a cheaper material. However, technical advances are becoming more important, providing replacement materials with improved specifications. For example, in the last few decades the use of cast iron pipes for gas and water supplies has been phased out by the substitution of pvc (polyvinyl chloride), which is considerably lighter and not susceptible to corrosion. Even though a substitute may cost more, it may be the preferred choice for other good reasons. The recent development and use of fibre optics to replace copper wire in telecommunications is a good example of substitution for practical reasons. To transmit as much information by copper wire would require a cable 10 times larger in cross-section than a fibre optic.

Another increasingly important reason for substitution is the minimization of adverse environmental effects, particularly relating to health. In recent years, many regulations have been introduced to provide a framework for industry to operate safely; they also provide the necessary motivation for change when the cost is high. Public opinion can also be very important, particularly if it can be turned to commercial advantage.

The toxicity of lead is the main reason why its use in paints has been — and in petrol is being — discontinued. Bismuth would be a possible substitute for lead in many applications where toxicity is a problem, because it has similar physical properties yet is non-toxic. This substitution has not yet happened, however, probably because bismuth is much more costly (about $5 000 per tonne) and has more limited availability. Plastics have replaced lead in building construction and cable coverings, and lighter metals have replaced it in containers.

An important effect of substitution is that it may bring about a change in the demand for a resource. A decrease in demand tends to drive prices down, profitability suffers and the supply industry declines. Alternatively, an increase in demand may drive up prices, leading to greater profitability and a thriving supply industry. Demand and prices depend on a multiplicity of factors — economic, political and technological. If prices drop too low it might only be viable to mine the richest of deposits.

Prices and demand are dependent not only on the usefulness of a metal, but also on the ease with which it can be supplied. In fact, the ultimate constraint on supply is the *availability* of a resource — the ease by which it can be obtained from the Earth, and from its ore. In the case of metals, their availability depends in part on their average abundance in the crust, but more importantly, on the extent to which they are concentrated by geological processes to form ore deposits, on how large and how common those deposits are.

Table 4 compares just one measure of the availability of metals — their crustal abundance — with their annual production and price. It is clear that iron, which is a major constituent of the Earth's crust, is produced in much larger quantities than any other metal and at by far the lowest price. That is because there are plenty of large, rich deposits from which ore may be extracted easily. Thus, iron is readily available, and because economies of scale in mining and extraction are possible, its price is low. In contrast, aluminium, which is slightly more abundant than iron in the crust, commands a much higher price (Table 4), because it is more costly to extract from its ore. Price can be low even if a metal has quite a low abundance, providing its ore is readily available and easily extractable; lead is an example. If demand is high, and availability scarce, as for the precious metals gold and platinum, then prices are especially high. The relationships between amounts of metals produced and their crustal abundance are more easily seen in Figure 4.

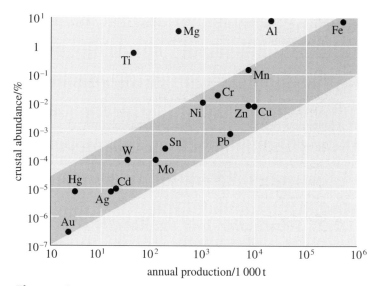

Figure 4   A graphical comparison between the annual amounts of metals produced from ores and their crustal abundance (data from Table 4). Most metals plot within the shaded band, which represents a constant range of abundance-to-production ratios. Note the log–log scale.

Table 4   The annual production, crustal abundance, average price and notional value of selected metals, based on data for 1992

Metal	Production/1 000 t	Abundance in continental crust/%	Average price/ $ per tonne	Notional value of world production/$ × 10⁹
iron	501 900	7.1	205	
aluminium	19 200	8.4	1 270	24.4
copper	9 290	0.007 5	2 290	21.3
zinc	7 140	0.008	1 240	8.85
manganese	7 100*	0.14	1 430	10.2
lead	3 200	0.000 8	540	1.73
chromium	1 800*	0.018 5	5 950	10.7
nickel	922	0.011	7 000	6.45
magnesium	304	3.2	3 310	1.01
tin	176	0.000 25	6 110	1.08
molybdenum	112	0.000 1	10 700	1.20
titanium	38.5	0.54	8 250	0.35
tungsten	31.5	0.000 1	7 310	0.23
cadmium	18.7	0.000 009 8	2 030	0.04
silver	15.3	0.000 008	127 000	1.90
mercury	3.0	0.000 008	5 860	0.02
gold	2.25	0.000 000 3	11 100 000	

* These estimates refer to the amounts of these metals that end up in metallic form; most sources quote production data for their ore minerals, pyrolusite and chromite.

○ How is the annual production (and use) of metals related to their crustal abundance?

○ In Figure 4 there is a linear relationship (the shaded band) between quantities of metals produced and their abundance in the crust. Although this broad trend is apparent from the data in Table 4, it is much clearer in Figure 4, where any data that do not fit the pattern are easier to identify. Interestingly, some of the *major elements* (Block 1, Section 3.2) in crustal rocks — aluminium, magnesium and titanium — are produced in much smaller quantities, whereas others — notably gold and lead — are produced in slightly greater quantities than might be expected from their crustal abundances.

Table 4 also reveals a broadly inverse relationship between price and crustal abundance. It should not be surprising that rarity tends to give rise to higher prices. However, the declining demand for lead, cadmium and mercury, largely in recognition of their toxicity, results in much lower prices than their low crustal abundances might suggest.

The production data in Table 4 show the overwhelming importance of iron: its production level is about ten times as much as that of *all* the other metals put together. The relatively high production level of manganese is mainly due to its use as a component of steel alloys. These statistics enable us to evaluate the relative importance of different metal resources, not only in terms of the amounts produced, but in terms of their *notional value* (production × price) to the world economy. The reason for calling it a notional value is because many metals such as manganese and chromium are produced mainly as a component of steels, not as the pure metal. These data represent only a snapshot in time, however, as both production and price respond to variations in demand from year to year.

Question 4

(a) Calculate the notional values of iron and gold production to the world economy in 1992 using data from Table 4. Enter your results in Table 4.

(b) Compare the combined notional value of those metals mainly used in steels — including manganese, chromium and nickel — with the notional value of the metals aluminium, copper and zinc, which are more often used as metals in their own right.

1.2 Where do metals come from?

If you pick up almost any rock, you might be surprised to know that it contains just about every natural chemical element there is. Most of them, however, are normally present only in vanishingly small, trace amounts, perhaps one atom in a million for some, and one in a billion, or even a thousand billion, for others. If we want to extract a particular metal from a rock, it is sensible (and energy efficient) to take advantage of *geological processes* that have unevenly distributed chemical elements in nature and have *concentrated* particular metals in particular rocks and minerals. However, to be a viable source of any metal, a rock must not only contain a relatively *high concentration* of the metal but it must be in a *form* suitable to make the effort of extraction and processing worthwhile. Any *rock* of this kind, from which metals can be extracted economically is known as an *ore*.

In what form, then, do metals occur naturally? Unfortunately, only a few metals are found naturally in their native, uncombined, state. As we learnt in Block 1, most metals occur combined with other elements in minerals, the most common being the rock-forming silicate minerals, such as olivines, pyroxenes, feldspars, clays and micas, from which metals are generally difficult to extract. Oxide, sulphide, and some carbonate minerals generally contain higher concentrations of metals, and are much more amenable to the extraction of metals through chemical processes, such as smelting (featured for iron in Video Band 1). Minerals like these, which can be used as an economic source of metals, are known as *ore minerals*, whether or not they occur in an ore deposit. Table 5 lists many of the more common ore minerals, grouped as sources of **major metals** (those produced in large quantities), **minor metals** (those produced in smaller quantities, often for specialized uses) and **precious metals** (those that are rare and command high prices).

For any *rock* to be an *ore* it must not only contain an ore mineral, but the ore mineral must be present in sufficient abundance for it to be separated economically. However, even rich ores contain minerals and rock that are not required. Such material is known as **gangue** (pronounced 'gang'), the worthless part of the ore that has to be mined in order to obtain the ore mineral(s). Expressed simply:

$$\text{ore} = \text{ore mineral} + \text{gangue}$$
$$\text{(rock)} \quad \text{(economic fraction)} \quad \text{(waste fraction)}$$

The proportions of ore, ore mineral concentrate (with most of the gangue removed) and pure metal produced from a typical copper deposit are shown in Figure 5. For many deposits, waste represents a large proportion of the ore. These relationships will be illustrated further in Section 1.3.

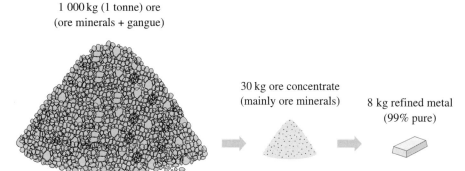

1 000 kg (1 tonne) ore
(ore minerals + gangue)

30 kg ore concentrate
(mainly ore minerals)

8 kg refined metal
(99% pure)

Figure 5 Relative quantities of ore, separated ore minerals and extracted metal for a typical copper deposit. Each pile contains the same amount of copper.

It is useful to make a distinction between a mineral deposit and an ore deposit. A **mineral deposit** is any naturally occurring concentration of potentially useful inorganic material, which may be of ore minerals or even rock (in the context of industrial minerals, such as the sands and gravels featured in Block 2). It may not be economically exploitable, unlike an ore deposit. An **ore deposit**, sometimes called an ore body, is much more restricted; it is a form of mineral deposit, or part of a mineral deposit, that contains ore, which is, by definition, economically exploitable.

The presence of more than one metal in an ore is quite common and is often important in ensuring the economic viability of an ore deposit. In many copper mines, for example, gold is often a **by-product**. Although volumetrically insignificant, it can be the most valuable product.

◐ What are the two most common types of ore mineral listed in Table 5?

◑ Oxide and sulphide ore minerals are dominant.

Table 5 The more important ore minerals of metals considered in this Block (the most commonly encountered ore minerals are shown in italics)

	Mineral, formula	Type of mineral
Major metals		
aluminium, Al	*bauxite*[†], e.g. $Al_2O_3.3H_2O$	hydrated oxide
chromium, Cr	*chromite, $(Fe,Mg)Cr_2O_4$*	oxide
copper, Cu	*chalcopyrite, $CuFeS_2$*; bornite, Cu_5FeS_4; covellite, CuS; chalcocite, Cu_2S	sulphide
	malachite, $CuCO_3.Cu(OH)_2$; azurite, $2CuCO_3.Cu(OH)_2$	carbonate/hydroxide
	cuprite, Cu_2O	oxide
	native copper, Cu	metal
iron, Fe	*magnetite, Fe_3O_4*; *haematite, Fe_2O_3*	oxide
	limonite, $Fe_2O_3.H_2O$	hydrated oxide
	siderite, $FeCO_3$	carbonate
	(*pyrite, FeS_2*; *pyrrhotite, FeS*)*; arsenopyrite, FeAsS	sulphide
lead, Pb	*galena, PbS*	sulphide
manganese, Mn	pyrolusite, MnO_2	oxide
zinc, Zn	*sphalerite, ZnS*	sulphide
Minor metals		
beryllium, Be	beryl, $Be_3Al_2(SiO_3)_6$	silicate
bismuth, Bi	bismuthinite, Bi_2S_3	sulphide
cadmium, Cd	substitution of Cd for Zn in sphalerite	sulphide
cerium, Ce	monazite, $(Ce,Th)PO_4$	phosphate
lithium, Li	spodumene, $LiAlSi_2O_6$	silicate
mercury, Hg	cinnabar, HgS	sulphide
molybdenum, Mo	*molybdenite, MoS_2*	sulphide
nickel, Ni	pentlandite, $(Ni,Fe)_9S_8$	sulphide
niobium, Nb	columbite, $FeNb_2O_6$	oxide
tantalum, Ta	tantalite, $FeTa_2O_6$	oxide
thorium, Th	monazite, $(Ce,Th)PO_4$	phosphate
	thorite, $ThSiO_4$	silicate
tin, Sn	*cassiterite, SnO_2*	oxide
titanium, Ti	*ilmenite, $FeTiO_3$*; *rutile, TiO_2*	oxide
tungsten, W	wolframite, $FeWO_4$	oxide
uranium, U	uraninite, UO_2 (sometimes quoted as U_3O_8)	oxide
vanadium, V	substitution of V for Fe in magnetite	oxide
zirconium, Zr	*zircon, $ZrSiO_4$*	silicate
Precious metals		
gold, Au	*native gold, Au*	metal
platinum, Pt	*native platinum, Pt*	metal
silver, Ag	acanthite, Ag_2S; minor component in galena	sulphide
	native silver, Ag; also naturally alloyed with gold	metal

* Pyrite and pyrrhotite are included because they are closely associated with many ore minerals. Currently they are not regarded as true ore minerals although pyrite has been used for sulphuric acid production.

† Strictly, bauxite is a rock containing hydrated aluminium hydroxide minerals.

There are two reasons for the dominance of oxide and sulphide ore minerals: firstly, metals can often be *more easily extracted* from oxide and sulphide minerals, and secondly, they usually contain *higher concentrations* of metal compared with many other types of mineral, such as silicates.

What may seem strange in Table 5 is that few metals form *both* oxide *and* sulphide ore minerals. In natural circumstances, most metals tend to form *either* oxides *or* sulphides. Part of the reason for this is a chemical one: the relative ease by which metal atoms combine with oxygen and sulphur atoms depends on how easily they lose electrons, a property known as *electronegativity* and explained further in the box 'Electronegativity', which draws on explanations of atomic structure from Block 1 (Section 3).

Many of the ore minerals in Table 5, such as galena (PbS) or sphalerite (ZnS), appear to be simple compounds. Their formulae correspond to the proportions of atoms present in their mineral structure, in which the atoms fit

Electronegativity

Electronegativity *is a measure of the ease by which atoms attract electrons.* A numerical scale for expressing electronegativity was developed by the American chemist Linus Pauling; values for the elements on his scale are given in Figure 6a. Notice that non-metals, which form *anions* such as Cl^-, O^{2-} and S^{2-}, by *taking up* electrons to fill their outer electron shell, have *higher* electronegativity than metals. Metals normally *give up* electrons to form *cations* such as Na^+, Mg^{2+} and Al^{3+}.

Electrons are more easily given up by metals nearest to the left-hand side of the Periodic Table to achieve a stable outer electron shell. Thus, we see from Figure 6a that values of electronegativity are especially *low* for the alkali metals and *high* for non-metals. Values generally increase across rows of the Periodic Table (Figure 6b) and decrease down Groups. Metals have a wide range of electronegativity values, however, with caesium having the lowest (0.8) and gold the highest (2.4). Compounds formed between two elements with *large differences in their electronegativity values* tend to have *strong ionic bonds*, as in common salt (NaCl). In contrast, bonding between two elements with *small differences in electronegativity* tends to be *covalent*, as in the gas nitrogen monoxide (NO); bonding between atoms of the same element in simple gases, such as nitrogen (N_2) and oxygen (O_2), is entirely covalent.

How does all this help to explain the tendency of metals to form either oxides or sulphides as their principal ore minerals? Well, the electronegativity of oxygen (3.5) is much greater than that of sulphur (2.5). Thus, oxygen atoms tend to take up electrons more readily than sulphur atoms. As a result, metals with *low* electronegativity values tend to form *ionic bonds* with oxygen (and preferentially form oxide minerals — Figure 6a), whereas the bonding between

metals with a *high* electronegativity and sulphur tends to be largely *covalent* (preferentially forming sulphide minerals — Figure 6a). Although there is no clear dividing line, metals with electronegativity values below 1.8 tend to form oxide minerals and those above 1.8 tend to form sulphide minerals. Around 1.8, they may form either, so iron is one of the few metals (Figure 6a) that commonly occurs either as the oxides, haematite (Fe_2O_3) and magnetite (Fe_3O_4), or as the sulphides, pyrite (FeS_2) and pyrrhotite (FeS). Elements with very high electronegativity such as gold (Au) and platinum (Pt) may form sulphides, but frequently remain uncombined, in their native state (Table 5).

◯ If lower values of electronegativity correspond to an increase in strength of ionic bonding in ore minerals, suggest which three of the metals mercury, aluminium, titanium, copper, silver and lithium should be relatively easy to extract from their ore minerals, and which three should be more difficult.

◯ The easier metals to extract are those that form the weaker ionic bonds — that is, those with a relatively high electronegativity, such as mercury, copper and silver, which normally form sulphide ore minerals. The most difficult metals to extract are those that form strong ionic bonds — that is, those with a relatively low electronegativity, such as lithium, aluminium and titanium, which occur as oxide ore minerals. (As noted in connection with Figure 4, some metals, such as aluminium, magnesium and titanium, are not produced in the quantities that might be expected from their crustal abundances; this is largely due to the difficulty and cost of extraction.)

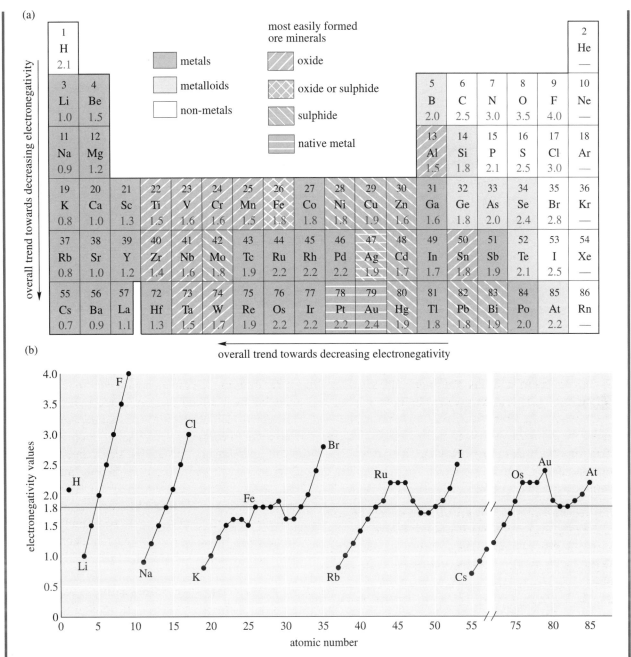

Figure 6 (a) Pauling electronegativity values for the elements (in colour), showing a broad variation across the Periodic Table, and which metals tend to form sulphide minerals, oxide minerals or both; (b) plot of electronegativities against atomic number, showing a marked but not quite regular increase in electronegativity across Periods.

together in a continuous, repeating arrangement to form a three-dimensional lattice. It was explained in Block 1 (Section 3.4.1) that atoms of similar size (ionic radius) and charge can substitute for each other in this lattice. For extensive substitution of one element by another to be possible, their *charges* must be identical so that charge balance is maintained, and their *sizes* must be similar so as not to disrupt the structure of the lattice. To help you to understand substitution better, complete the following Activity, which involves studying Figure 7, a plot showing the size (in picometres, pm) and the effective ionic charge* of many common metal ions.

---

* In reality, no ion with a charge greater than 3+ can exist under normal conditions because the energy to remove more than three electrons from an atom is too great. What is important, however, is the number of electrons *available* for bonding — both ionic and covalent — and this is expressed by the term 'effective ionic charge'; the associated 'ion' size is given by the term 'effective ionic radius'. This allows us to consider the possibilities for metal substitution in minerals. For convenience, we shall usually omit the word 'effective'.

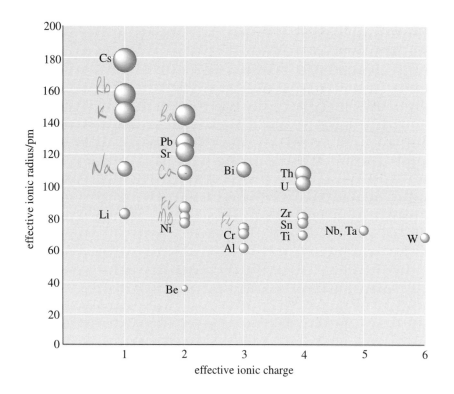

Figure 7 Plot of effective ionic charge against effective ionic radius for selected metals. Elements with similar ionic radius and the same ionic charge are more likely to substitute for each other in minerals.

Activity 2 Ionic substitution

(a) Identify and label on Figure 7 the spheres that represent the following ions:

(i) Na^+ (110 pm), K^+ (146 pm), Ca^{2+} (108 pm) — how do they relate to each other?

(ii) Mg^{2+} (80 pm), Fe^{2+} (86 pm), Fe^{3+} (73 pm) — how do they relate to each other (note that iron is a metal whose ions can carry different charges)?

(iii) Ba^{2+} (144 pm), Rb^+ (157 pm) — how do they relate to Na^+ and K^+?

(b) How do the ionic radii of more highly charged ions compare with those of ions with small charges in Figure 7? Why do you think ionic radii are smaller for more highly charged ions? (*Hint* This point was made in Audio Band 1: *Elements and the Periodic Table*.)

(c) Both iron and lead form sulphide ore minerals — pyrrhotite (FeS) and galena (PbS), respectively. In which of these minerals do you think nickel would more readily substitute?

Olivines exhibit the simplest form of substitution in minerals: they form a complete range of *solid solution* compositions between the **end members**, forsterite (Mg_2SiO_4) and fayalite (Fe_2SiO_4), involving exchange between Mg^{2+} (80 pm) and Fe^{2+} (86 pm), ions of like charge and similar size. See where they are located in Figure 7. Less ideal substitution is a feature of the alkali feldspars, which form an incomplete range of solid solution compositions between the end members, albite ($NaAlSi_3O_8$) and orthoclase ($KAlSi_3O_8$). Only limited amounts of exchange occur between Na^+ (110 pm) and K^+ (146 pm). Notice that these ions have the same charges but somewhat different sizes (Figure 7) — the reason for the *incomplete* range of solid solution compositions in the alkali feldspars.

A slightly more complex form of substitution occurs when *two* different ions substitute for two others, their *combined* charges and sizes matching those of the ions that they are substituting. This is known as **coupled substitution** and occurs in the plagioclase feldspars, which form a *complete* range of solid solution compositions between the end members, albite ($NaAlSi_3O_8$) and anorthite ($CaAl_2Si_2O_8$). This substitution involves the ion pairs Na^+Si^{4+} and $Ca^{2+}Al^{3+}$ to maintain charge balance.

Examining Figure 7 in more detail, it is easy to see groups of ions with similar ionic radii and the same charge, within which substitution is possible.

○ The composition of the ore mineral, chromite, $(Fe,Mg)Cr_2O_4$, is often slightly more complicated than its formula suggests. It usually contains not only iron, magnesium and chromium but also aluminium. Using Figure 7, decide which of the dominant ions, Fe^{2+} and Cr^{3+}, would be substituted by Al^{3+}.

○ Al^{3+} will substitute for Cr^{3+} because it has the same charge and a similar ionic radius.

Similar substitutions arise among the major constituents of some ore minerals, such as the solid solutions involving Fe^{2+} and Ni^{2+} in pentlandite $((Ni,Fe)_9S_8)$, Zn^{2+} and Fe^{2+} in sphalerite (ZnS), and Cu^{2+} and Fe^{2+} in chalcopyrite ($CuFeS_2$). However, it is one thing for substitution to be *theoretically* possible, but quite another for it to *occur* in practice. That depends firstly on the *availability* of the potentially substituting element, and then on whether it prefers to occupy *alternative sites* in other minerals.

○ Iron and magnesium commonly substitute for each other in silicate minerals, but magnesium does not substitute for iron in its sulphide minerals pyrrhotite (FeS) and pyrite (FeS_2). How can we explain this?

○ The electronegativity of magnesium (1.2) is low, so it forms oxide ore minerals in nature and not sulphides. The electronegativity of iron (1.8) is sufficiently high for it to form either oxides or sulphide minerals, depending on the availability of oxygen and sulphur during crystallization.

When major elements are substituted in *small amounts* by trace elements, ionic size is most important; small differences in charge can often be tolerated. Although Ba^{2+} (144 pm) has a different charge, it has a similar ionic radius to K^+ (146 pm), and, like Rb^+ (157 pm), may substitute in alkali feldspars. Of the minerals listed in Table 5, the occurrence of cadmium in sphalerite and vanadium in magnetite are examples where trace element substitution is important in ore minerals. Therefore, although minerals are normally written with simple chemical formulae, as in Table 5, we should be aware that they are commonly more complex and may contain *additional* minor constituents. For example, sphalerite may contain up to 10% FeS and 1% CdS. In these circumstances we should strictly write the formula of sphalerite as $(Zn_{0.89},Fe_{0.10},Cd_{0.01})S$ to account for these substitutions, rather than ZnS. When writing formulae, it is often convenient to ignore these small components.

During ore processing, especially smelting, substituted elements become *impurities*, which can be a problem and may reduce the value of an ore. Cadmium, for example, has no ore mineral of its own, and is obtained from sphalerite, so it might be regarded as a beneficial by-product. However, it is also a highly toxic metal, which can create severe health problems if it contaminates crops and enters the food chain. Thus, safeguarding the environment adds to the cost both of zinc smelting and cadmium production. When they can be usefully extracted as by-products, impurities can enhance the value of an ore. A particularly valuable example is the occurrence of silver in galena (PbS). Even at a silver concentration of only 1%, it has often been the main reason for mining galena, since silver is of far greater value than the lead itself. Impurities in ores can also come from gangue minerals that are difficult to separate. The mineral arsenopyrite (FeAsS), for example, is often associated with copper and zinc sulphides. In early smelting of copper ores, its presence was of benefit, as it produced arsenical copper, which is harder than pure copper; but when smelting took place on a large scale, the toxicity of arsenic released into the air became an environmental hazard.

Question 5

Taking account of their ionic charges and ionic radii, which of the following ions Ba^{2+} (144 pm), Fe^{3+} (73 pm), Rb^+ (157 pm), Fe^{2+} (86 pm), Ti^{4+} (69 pm), Bi^{3+} (110 pm) and Nb^{5+} (72 pm) could substitute for tin, Sn^{4+} (77 pm), and therefore might be present as impurities in cassiterite (SnO_2).

1.3   What is an ore deposit?

We have already established that an ore is a rock from which metal can be extracted economically. Usually, the first step in recognizing an *ore deposit* is to confirm the presence of *ore minerals*, such as those in Table 5, which contain metals in economically extractable concentrations. Once the ore mineralogy has been determined, it is the *concentration of the metal* that can be extracted by economic methods, its *grade*, and the distribution of that grade which must be evaluated to define the extent of an ore body. For most ores, grade is expressed in weight per cent (wt %) of the metal, or, sometimes, the dominant ore mineral, but for precious metals with low crustal abundances, grade is usually measured in grams per tonne ($g\,t^{-1}$, numerically equivalent to parts per million, ppm). In this Block, concentrations in wt % will be written as % for brevity.

⬤   If 20 kg of copper could be extracted from 1 tonne (1 000 kg) of rock, what would be its grade?

⬤ $$Grade = \frac{mass\ of\ extractable\ metal\ in\ rock}{mass\ of\ rock} \times 100\%$$

In this example, the grade = $\dfrac{20 \times 100\%}{1\,000}$ = 2% copper

Strictly, an ore body is defined in terms of rock in which the grade of metal is high enough to be mined economically, in other words, is above *cut-off grade* (Block 1, Section 2.2). Since cut-off grade is defined in economic terms, it is dependent on *world conditions*, such as market price, as well as *local factors*, such as the presence of valuable by-products, or the costs of environmental protection. It also depends on the scale and form of the mining operation, with which the ratio of fixed to variable costs (discussed in Block 1) varies. The initial investment in equipment and developing a working infrastructure before a mine starts production involves mainly fixed costs. The size of investment depends on the type of deposit, especially its extent, and the type of mining, whether underground or open pit. These considerations will be examined further in *Metals 2*.

Reserves were defined in Block 1 as quantities of a resource that can be extracted profitably and legally under existing conditions. In practical terms, it is the amount of ore that exceeds the *cut-off grade*. Because cut-off grade, and therefore the size of an ore deposit and the reserves it contains, all vary with economic circumstances, it is important to appreciate how much reserves can vary with changes in cut-off grade. Activity 3 examines how the size and form of an ore deposit might vary with cut-off grade through an evaluation of *size–grade relationships* for contrasting types of mineral deposit. At one extreme, there are **dispersed deposits**, in which ore minerals are distributed at *low grades* throughout *large volumes* of rock. At the other extreme are **confined deposits**, in which ore minerals are concentrated at *high grade* in relatively *small volumes* of rock. You will see that the way reserves change with cut-off grade and the factors that define available reserves are quite different in each case.

Activity 3 Size–grade relationships for dispersed and confined ore deposits

(i)   Dispersed deposits

Figure 8a is an example of an idealized dispersed deposit, where the grade of copper (shown by the pattern of grade contours) decreases gradually and progressively away from the centre of the deposit. Table 6a shows how the average grade and size of the ore body would vary if each of these contours were the cut-off grade.

(a) For cut-off grades of 0.6% and 0.4%, and from the average grade and reserves of ore given, calculate the reserves of metal. Write your answers in Table 6a.

(b) With increasing *size* of such a dispersed ore body, how do its average grade, the corresponding reserves of ore and the reserves of metal vary?

Figure 8   Block diagrams showing the distribution of metal grades in typical examples of (a) dispersed, and (b) confined deposits.

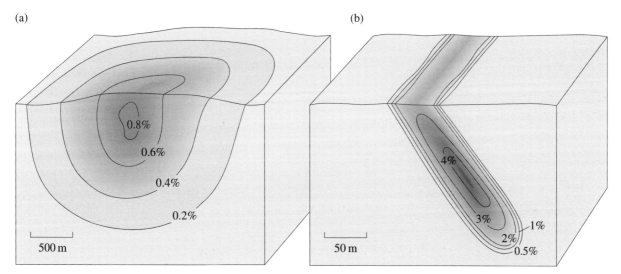

(a)

(b)

500 m

50 m

0.8%
0.6%
0.4%
0.2%

4%
3%
2%
1%
0.5%

Table 6   An example of the variation of average grade, reserves of ore and reserves of metal with changing cut-off grade for typical dispersed and confined deposits featured in Figure 8

(a) Dispersed deposit				(b) Confined deposit			
Cut-off grade/%	Average grade of reserves/%	Reserves of ore/Mt	Reserves of metal/Mt	Cut-off grade/%	Average grade of reserves/%	Reserves of ore/Mt	Reserves of metal/Mt
0.8	2.0	50	1.0	4.0	5.0	0.04	0.002
0.6	0.8	250	*2.0*	3.0	3.3	0.3	
0.4	0.5	800	*4.0*	2.0	2.5	0.8	
0.2	0.4	2 000	8.0	1.0	2.2	1.0	
				0.5	2.1	1.1	0.023

⬤ At a cut-off grade of 0.8% Cu, what would be the shape of the ore body and the amount of reserves it contains.

_____

◯ The ore body would occupy the roughly spherical region within the 0.8% contour, which amounts to a reserve of 50 Mt of ore at an average grade of 2%. It would contain $50 \times 0.02 = 1$ Mt of copper metal.

(c) If economic conditions changed and the cut-off grade for this dispersed deposit were only 0.4% Cu, how would the size of the deposit change compared with a cut-off grade of 0.8% Cu (described above), in terms of the amounts of ore and the reserves of copper it contains? What would be the difference in the amount of waste produced (assuming copper could be extracted directly)?

(ii) Confined deposits

The distribution of metal grades for a typical confined deposit is illustrated in Figure 8b. Data are given in Table 6b in the same format as for dispersed deposits. Notice that the scale here is quite different compared with the dispersed deposit, and, although the grades and average grades are much *greater*, the reserves of metal are much *smaller*.

(d) For cut-off grades of 3%, 2% and 1%, and from the average grade and reserves of ore given, calculate the reserves of metal. Answer in Table 6b.

Grade–tonnage charts

The variation of metal reserves with cut-off grade for a deposit can be illustrated graphically by plotting grade–tonnage charts, Figure 9a and 9b, from the data in Table 6a and b, respectively.

(e) For the dispersed deposit, complete the plot of cut-off grade against reserves of metal on Figure 9a.

⬤ What kind of curve is this? How do reserves of metal vary with decreasing cut-off grade?

_____

◯ It is an exponential curve (Block 1, Section 1.3). For successively lower cut-off grades, reserves of metal increase dramatically.

Figure 9 Grade–tonnage graphs, showing variation of metal reserves with cut-off grade, for the (a) dispersed and (b) confined deposits featured in Figure 8a and 8b.

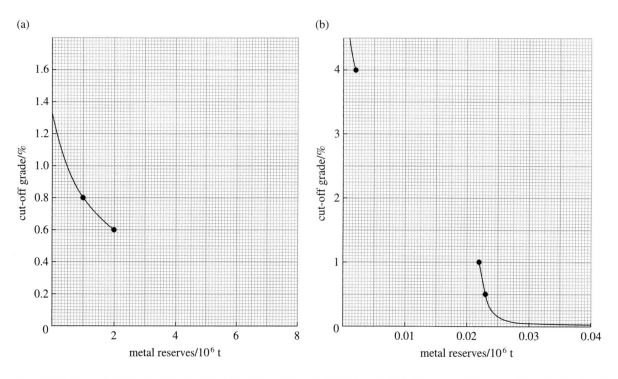

(a)

cut-off grade/%

metal reserves/10^6 t

(b)

cut-off grade/%

metal reserves/10^6 t

(f) Complete the grade–tonnage chart (Figure 9b) for the confined deposit.

The completed curve in Figure 9b is more complex than that in Figure 9a, but it does indicate that mining beyond a grade of 2% (where the curve steepens) would add little to reserves, because the grade falls so rapidly at the margins of the deposit. Whether the cut-off grade for the confined deposit is 2% or 0.5% makes little difference to the reserves.

Activity 3 demonstrates an important distinction between dispersed and confined deposits — how their reserves vary with cut-off grade. The extent of a confined ore body is therefore controlled mainly by *geological factors*, whereas the extent of a dispersed ore body is controlled mainly by the *cut-off grade*, and therefore varies with economic circumstances. In addition, the large *scale* of the dispersed deposit allows it to be mined at lower cut-off grade than for the smaller, confined deposit. Modern, mechanized, large-scale mining methods with efficient means of recovery have enabled cut-off grades of many metals to be reduced over the years so that low-grade, large-volume deposits can often be mined profitably today. Such methods are less of an advantage for small, high-grade confined deposits.

Cut-off grade marks the limit of profitable extraction at a *particular mining location*. When cut-off grades are averaged for all mines *world wide*, a guide value called the *average minimum exploitable grade* is obtained. Table 7 lists the average minimum exploitable grades for a number of important metals alongside their average crustal abundances. To be worth mining, metals must be concentrated by geological processes to levels well above their crustal abundance. The extent of their enrichment is known as their *concentration factor*. Because ores are normally mined on land, an average continental crust composition is used in Table 7 to calculate these enrichments.

Table 7 The average minimum exploitable grades, abundance in continental crust, concentration factors and prices of common metals

Metal	Average minimum exploitable grade/%	Abundance in continental crust/%	Concentration factor	Average metal price 1992/$ t^{-1}
iron	55	7.1	7.7	205
aluminium	30	8.4	3.6	1 270
lead	5	0.000 8	6 250	540
zinc	3	0.008		1 240
nickel	1	0.011		7 000
copper	0.5	0.007 5		2 290
tin	0.5	0.000 25		6 110
mercury	0.2	0.000 008	25 000	5 860
silver	0.01	0.000 008	1 250	127 000
gold	0.000 4	0.000 000 3		11 100 000

Question 6

For the metals zinc, nickel, copper, tin and gold, use data in Table 7 to calculate the concentration factors required to form ore deposits from average continental crust. Fill in the gaps in Table 7.

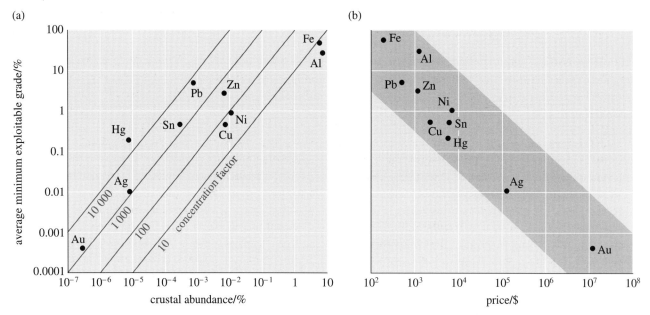

Is there any correlation between crustal averages and average minimum exploitable grade? Table 7 appears to show a broad trend, but not a particularly close correlation. Hence concentration factors vary widely, from 3.6 up to 25 000. These relationships are shown graphically in Figure 10a.

Average minimum exploitable grades reflect a number of factors — not only the crustal abundance of the metal, but also the extent to which metals can be enriched by geological processes to form ore deposits. The processes that bring about these concentrations and why some should be more efficient than others are an important part of this Block. The extent of natural concentration for each metal is reflected in their concentration factors (Figure 10a). However, average minimum exploitable grades, like cut-off grade, also depend on economic factors. If there are not enough high-grade reserves available to satisfy demand, lower grades will be exploited even though the cost may be higher.

Figure 10 A graphical comparison between the average minimum exploitable grades for metals and (a) their crustal abundances, extending across a wide range of concentration factors, and (b) their prices, which fall in a linear shaded band. Note that both graphs have log–log scales (data from Table 7).

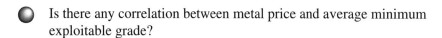 Is there any correlation between metal price and average minimum exploitable grade?

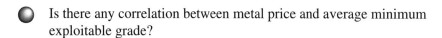 Yes. Figure 10b shows there is quite a good correlation — in this case an inverse one, in which minimum exploitable grade decreases as price increases because metal price is the main economic factor that determines minimum exploitable grade.

A higher price will permit exploitation of lower-grade material because it will be possible to finance the additional processing needed to extract the metal. Gold can be worked profitably at very low grades; mercury cannot. For relatively abundant metals, such as iron and aluminium, only high-grade ores are economic to work. If such high-grade ores were not available, lower grades might be used if the higher costs of separation and extraction could be supported by higher prices.

1.4 Environmental aspects of metals

1.4.1 Metals in the environment

Metals are not only important for their uses as metals. Metallic elements are an integral part of our natural environment and the make-up of all living organisms (see box 'Metals — the essence of life?'). However, some metallic elements and compounds of metals can be very damaging to many forms of life.

Metals — the essence of life?

Metals constitute less than 1% of the atoms in the human body. The most abundant are sodium, potassium, calcium and magnesium — which are also the most abundant metals in seawater. Many metals are *essential* to our good health, and, indeed, to our very existence. Sodium helps our nerves transmit messages and our muscles to contract. A shortage, caused by excessive sweating, can lead to cramp. Calcium is required to form and harden our bones. An inability to absorb calcium (often due to vitamin D deficiency) can cause children's bones to remain soft and become deformed, a disease known as rickets. Less than 0.1% of atoms in the human body are trace elements; they include chromium, manganese, iron, cobalt, copper, zinc and molybdenum. These metals are *essential* as micronutrients, although the body's requirements are minute. Iron is present in haemoglobin — the red pigment and oxygen carrier in blood. Shortage of iron reduces haemoglobin levels and leads to anaemia, resulting in tiredness and lack of energy through shortage of oxygen to all parts of the body.

Supplies of all these **essential metals** are normally provided by a balanced diet. There are also **non-essential metals**, which have no nutritional benefits; they include barium, lead and tin. Some non-essential metals, like lead, are toxic; others, which have no adverse effects on health, are sometimes used as *additives* in foods, such as E173, better known as aluminium, E174 silver, and E175 gold, which provide metallic surface colours in confectionery (for example in cake decoration).

The lack of an essential element can give rise to health problems (through deficiency), but so too can an excess (through toxicity). There is usually a limited range of intakes over which an essential element contributes positively to the healthy functioning of an organism, as illustrated schematically in Figure 11. Table 8 quotes levels of dietary intake, toxic intake, and human body content of several metals, demonstrating that the human metabolism can handle — indeed requires — high levels of sodium and calcium, and much greater concentrations of essential trace metals such as iron and zinc than it does of non-essential metals such as tin and lead. Although tin is a non-essential element, its inorganic compounds are relatively non-toxic, but average body contents are lower for tin than for lead, which tends to concentrate in bones and teeth.

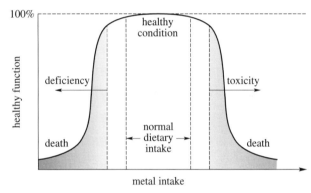

Figure 11 Schematic illustration of the metals intake–healthy function response curve for essential elements in living organisms.

Table 8 Levels of human intake of selected trace metals

Metal	Dietary range* /mg per day	Toxic intake* /mg per day	Amount in 70 kg person/mg
Essential metals			
sodium	2 000–15 000	non-toxic	100 000
calcium	600–1 400	non-toxic	1 000 000
magnesium	250–380	3 000	19 000
iron	6–40	200	4 200
zinc	5–40	150–600	2 300
copper	0.5–6	>250	72
molybdenum	0.05–0.35	5	—
cobalt	0.005–1.8	500	1.5
Non-essential metals			
barium	0.6–1.7	200	22
tin	0.2–3.5	2 000	14
lead	0.06–0.5	1	120
cadmium	0.007–3	3–330	50
mercury	0.004–0.02	0.4	—
silver	0.001 4–0.08	60	—

* Dietary ranges and toxicities are not accurately known.
Note Dietary ranges are not recommended intakes; average intakes usually fall at the low end of the range quoted.

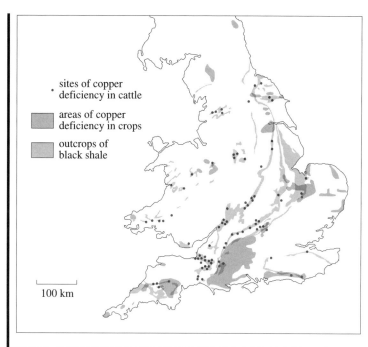

sites of copper
deficiency in cattle

areas of copper
deficiency in crops

outcrops of
black shale

100 km

It is also important for intake of metals to be balanced. In England and Wales, areas of copper deficiency in cattle surprisingly do not coincide with areas of copper deficiency in crops (Figures 12). The problem for animals, it seems, is not due to copper shortage in their food supply, but the presence of underlying black shales (also shown in Figure 12), which are rich in many trace metals, notably molybdenum. The molybdenum causes copper to precipitate in the gut of animals as highly insoluble compounds (such as $CuMoS_4$), which prevents essential copper being absorbed into the blood. This leads to symptoms of copper deficiency such as stunted growth, diarrhoea, anaemia, and damage to nerves.

Figure 12 Areas of England and Wales where copper deficiency occurs in cattle and in crops, and where black shales outcrop.

Whether the effects of a particular metal in the environment are beneficial or harmful to life depends on how much is available (Figure 11). For plants and animals, the presence of trace metals in soils can be essential as nutrients, whereas deficiencies can lead to health problems, and excessive amounts may also be harmful. Excessive metal concentrations may arise through discharge of mine waters or the dumping of wastes containing ore minerals and gangue. Some metal-based substances, particularly those containing heavy metals (such as cadmium, mercury and lead), can be extremely toxic, even in small quantities, particularly when they are in a water-soluble form which can be taken up by plants and animals. Organic compounds of lead (such as tetraethyl-lead) and mercury (such as methylmercury) are easily absorbed in body fats, and concentrate around organs such as the liver, where they are particularly damaging. In its metallic state, lead is fairly unreactive unless eaten, and, fortunately, most lead minerals occurring naturally are very insoluble in cool surface water and groundwater. Many of the worst examples of metal pollution are caused by waste from the chemicals industry; but in this Block, and more especially in Metals 2, we shall confine ourselves to the environmental impacts of the metal resources extraction and processing industries.

In the UK, there has been contamination of soils by mining for metals (now mostly discontinued) and associated industrial activity since the beginning of the Industrial Revolution. Figure 13a shows areas of England and Wales where stream sediments contain high levels of lead. Because stream sediment is a composite sample of the erosion products of rock and soil from upstream, these results suggest that high lead levels may occur extensively in the soils of England and Wales. Figure 13b shows areas of England and Wales where the *base metals* lead, copper and zinc have been mined. (The term **base metals** was originally used for metals low in value compared with gold and silver.)

○ Do the areas enriched with lead (Figure 13a) generally correlate with the location of the base metal mining fields (Figure 13b)?

○ Yes, although some of the high-level lead anomalies in Figure 13a lie outside base metal mining areas, and cannot be attributed either to the natural weathering of lead ores or to mining contamination.

(a)

100 km

(b)

100 km

The area of lead enrichment found in the lower Swansea valley (Figure 13a) is not related to a mining field, but to smelting and is therefore at least partly attributable to the extraction of lead from its ore. It was cheaper to transport lead ore from south-west England and mid-Wales to the coal in south Wales for smelting than the reverse. Another source of lead in the environment, on which attention has focused recently, is vehicle exhaust fumes, which has contaminated roadside soils and road dust across the whole country, and may contribute to elevated levels in some localities.

Figure 13 Areas of England and Wales showing (a) where stream sediments are enriched in lead, and (b) where base metal mining fields were located.

Lead toxicity was certainly a problem in parts of the UK at the time it was mined. Early nineteenth-century literature describes how, in Derbyshire, fumes from lead smelters poisoned plants for a quarter of a mile or more around smelter sites, and one account from 1817 describes the poisoning of cattle, sheep, poultry and dogs. Humans living near or working in smelters commonly suffered from symptoms given names such as 'lead-colic' and 'mill-reak'. Lead poisoning gives rise to anaemia, weakness, colic and paralysis; and low levels once thought to be safe are now believed to reduce intelligence, and impair memory and motor development, especially in children. Today, mining activity in Derbyshire has largely ceased, but the lead previously released into the environment persists in the soil. The full implications to humans now living in such contaminated areas, however, are not known.

Figure 14 Concentrations of copper in agricultural soil around mine spoil from an example in south-west England.

A similar story can be told for south-west England, which was the premier centre of mining in the world during much of the eighteenth and nineteenth centuries. Here, ore production, primarily for tin and copper, but also for other elements such as arsenic, lead and zinc, has left a legacy of dereliction and many potential sources of contamination of the surrounding agricultural land. Figure 14 shows an example of contamination from mine spoil. Levels of copper above a background value of about 150 ppm demonstrate contamination to at least 200 m away from the spoil heap. The topsoil is generally more

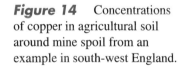

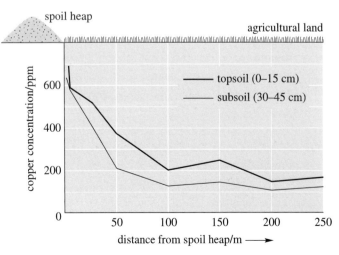

contaminated than the subsoil because contamination from the spoil heap is spread more easily over the surface than by seepage through the soil. The extent of mineralization and mining activity was so great in south-west England that over $1\,000\,km^2$ of land has been contaminated with one or more of the elements arsenic, copper, lead and zinc.

1.4.2 *Natural recycling, sustainability, and conservation of metals*

Metals occurring naturally, mostly in combined form in minerals and rocks or in solution (especially seawater), take part in all the geological processes that are responsible for moulding our global environment. Although these geological processes recycle Earth materials — through the rock cycle (Block 1, Section 3.5.4); the water cycle (Block 3, Section 2); and the carbon cycle (Block 4 Part 1, Section 2) — the time-scale of geological recycling of most metals, like the formation of fossil fuels, is extremely long in relation to the rates at which metals are being mined by humans and the predicted lifetimes of metal resources (Block 1, Section 2.5). Certain forms of metals extraction — for example of magnesium and even lithium from seawater — are arguably sustainable, however, because they are continually being replenished by natural processes.

In general, however, metal ores are being consumed faster than they are naturally replenished and must be regarded as non-renewable resources.

○   Although the sustainable exploitation of ore deposits indefinitely is not possible, in what ways can you imagine the lifetimes (i.e. reserves/ annual production) of metals being extended?

○   (i) By finding new reserves;

(ii) by improving extraction methods to exploit progressively lower-grade deposits;

(iii) by conservation to reduce usage and hence production — either through substitution of metals by other materials, or by recycling of metals themselves.

(i)   *Exploration techniques* are becoming more and more refined and very successful, especially at finding hidden deposits (as you will learn in *Metals 2*), but one day, all of the Earth's surface and the accessible subsurface will have been explored, and there will be no new deposits to find. For most metals, however, this time is likely to be a long way off.

(ii) *Extraction methods* are also becoming more efficient, but there is likely to be a limit to the minimum grade at which metal recovery would be economic, because energy demands increase with the processing of lower grades. If energy costs were to increase dramatically, minimum exploitable grades would increase too.

(iii) *Recycling* is usually energy efficient, but total recycling is impossible on account of wastage in manufacturing and use. Recycling on a domestic scale was discussed in Block 1 — but how extensive is recycling of metals on a global scale? This question can be assessed through Table 9 by comparing mine, or *primary*, production of a range of metals, with quantities of recovered scrap, or *secondary* production.

The quantities of scrap metal recycled (Table 9) are surprisingly high, probably reflecting recycling opportunities at various stages of manufacture, rather than amounts recycled after use. The advantage of recycling manufacturing waste is that it often needs only simple separation before being returned to the refinery. Recycling of used materials is more difficult, partly because metals leave manufacturing in many different forms. They may be alloyed, or coated onto other metals or plastics, or even chemically combined. They are also generally dispersed at low concentrations, and thus difficult to separate and recycle. Many metal products may be used and re-used over long periods of time, and when no longer useful they may not be reclaimable. For example, sheet steel often corrodes to form rust, which flakes off and wears away. Metals in *uncombined form* and in products that have relatively *short lives* are particularly suitable for recycling. Packaging used for foodstuffs, such as 'tin' and aluminium cans, is ideal.

Table 9 Comparison of world primary production (mined) and secondary production (scrap recovery) for a selection of important metals in 1992

Metal	Primary production/1 000 t	Secondary production/1 000 t	Proportion recycled/ % of total production
iron	501 000	300 130	37.4
aluminium	19 453	6 265	24.4
copper	9 254	4 595	33.2
zinc	7 245	1 543	17.6
lead	2 985	2 435	
tin	176	35	16.6
silver*	11.3	2.1	15.7
gold*	1.84	0.44	19.3

* Data for silver and gold are for Western countries only.

Question 7

Using Table 9, answer the following questions:

(a) What percentage of total lead production is recycled? Complete the Table. How does it compare with other metals listed?

(b) Considering the main uses of lead shown in Figure 2, suggest why so much lead can be recycled.

(c) Which form of lead use in Figure 2 is impossible to recycle and liable to be harmful to the environment?

1.5 Geological framework of elemental enrichment

The presence of ore deposits depends on the concentration of metals by geological **fractionation** processes — that is, natural processes that cause compositionally distinct fractions to separate. It should not be surprising that natural geological processes have this capability because many of the rock types encountered earlier in this Course are the result of fractionation processes involving selective separation of minerals which leads to element enrichment. Fractionated sediments include quartz sands, clays, evaporites, limestones and coal, where enrichments are due to sedimentary and weathering processes. These processes will be considered further in discussion of the formation of ore deposits at the Earth's surface in Section 3. In addition, we shall see that concentration of metals to form ore deposits can also occur by igneous fractionation processes (Section 2) and by fractionation involving hot, watery solutions (Section 4).

In these later Sections, we shall discover that element concentration is not unusual in geological processes, but to form an ore deposit usually requires processes to be developed in the extreme, which is not so common. The origins of element enrichment and ore deposit formation can be examined systematically through the mnemonic 'SADE', representing the *Source* of metals, the *Agent* of transportation, the site and cause of *Deposition*, and the *Energy* to drive the system (as introduced in Block 1, Section 3.6). Figure 15 shows schematically how these parts of an ore-forming system are linked. Let's look at each aspect in turn.

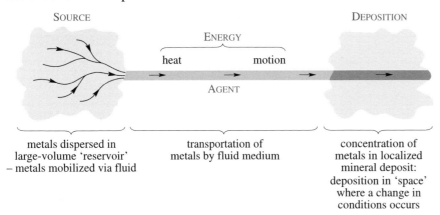

Figure 15 Schematic relationship between Source, Agent, Deposition and Energy involved in element enrichment. Although the spatial relationships shown are not entirely appropriate for all forms of ore deposit, the principles are generally applicable.

1.5.1 Aspects of SADE

Sources

The sources of metals that give rise to ore deposits (shown schematically in Figure 15) are the large-scale long-term geochemical reservoirs of the Earth, namely the mantle, the crust of continental and oceanic regions, and the oceans themselves. Here we are interested in the chemical compositions of these reservoirs, which are illustrated in Figure 16. The most important in terms of resources is the *crust*, because the resources of the crust are the most accessible. The mantle is also relevant because it is a source of new material which is continually being added to the crust through igneous activity at both constructive and destructive plate boundaries. You may recall from Block 1, Section 3.2 that crust is generated by magmatic activity at mid-ocean ridges where sea-floor spreading occurs, and at volcanic arcs which form above subduction zones where oceanic plates sink back into the mantle.

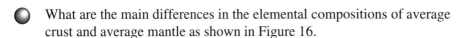 What are the main differences in the elemental compositions of average crust and average mantle as shown in Figure 16.

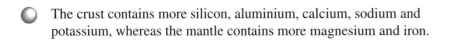 The crust contains more silicon, aluminium, calcium, sodium and potassium, whereas the mantle contains more magnesium and iron.

The differences in composition of the Earth's crust and mantle are a reflection of the geological fractionation processes that have formed the crust, the mass of which is insignificant compared with that of the mantle (Figure 16). There are also significant differences between the compositions of continental crust and oceanic crust, which are important where sources of metals are concerned. Indeed, within each of these crustal zones there is a wide range of rock types, many of which you have already encountered, and, like limestone and shale (Block 2, Section 5.2.2), may have very different compositions.

Many of the metals that are mined as ores are normally present only as trace elements in rocks (see their crustal abundances in Table 4). So how might the major element composition of the Earth (in Figure 16) control the distribution of those trace metals? Well, trace elements usually substitute to a

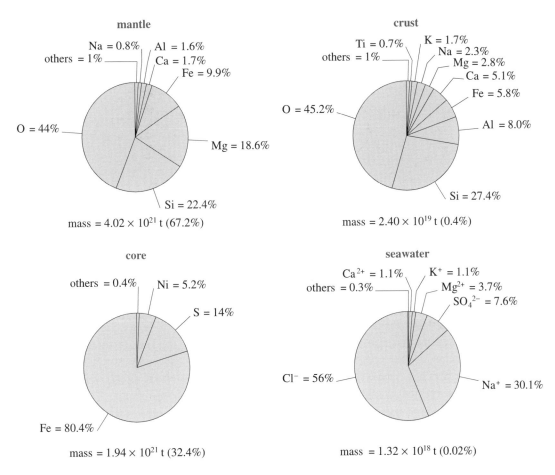

Figure 16 Proportions of major elements in the Earth's main geochemical reservoirs: the core, the mantle, the crust and seawater (as a proportion of its dissolved constituents — totalling 3.5%). Excluding the Earth's core, the main constituents of the solid Earth are oxygen and silicon. Other elements comprise roughly a quarter in total.

small extent for major elements in rock-forming minerals rather than form minerals of their own (Section 1.2). Thus, chromium and nickel, which often substitute for iron and magnesium, are preferentially concentrated in mantle rocks, which are rich in the ferromagnesian minerals, olivine and pyroxene. Barium and lead, on the other hand, tend to substitute into feldspars, which are much more abundant in crustal rocks.

Seawater is also a kind of reservoir for metals. The main ones are sodium, magnesium, calcium and potassium, which form soluble chlorides and sulphates and are largely responsible for the salinity of seawater (Figure 16). These *salts** may crystallize out of seawater to form evaporites (Block 2, Section 6), rocks that may be regarded as the ores of these metals. The salinity of seawater is maintained both through supply of salts from rivers and by evaporation from the oceans. However, as we shall find in later Sections, seawater is probably more important as an *agent* of extraction, transportation and concentration than as a *source* of ore-forming metals.

Agents

Essentially, agents provide the means by which metals can be removed from their source and transported to a site of deposition (Figure 15), and may be responsible for their concentration to form an ore deposit. Agents may

---

* A salt is an ionic compound, which can be formed by reaction of metal ions with an acid. Thus, sodium chloride (NaCl, common salt) is the sodium salt of hydrochloric acid (HCl) and calcium sulphate ($CaSO_4$, anhydrite) is the calcium salt of sulphuric acid (H_2SO_4).

operate physically, by transporting material, such as mineral grains, or chemically, by interacting with rocks to form a solution. Critical properties of any agent, therefore, are its mobility and its ability to carry metals.

 What natural substances are mobile and, therefore, potential agents?

 Magma, water and air.

Magmas form when hot rocks of the Earth's crust or mantle melt. Their low density makes them buoyant and, together with their fluidity, enables them to rise and migrate away from their source, sometimes to erupt at the surface and form volcanoes. Magmas are generally rich in major element metals, such as iron and aluminium, but are poor in trace element metals, such as tin and gold. A variety of physical and chemical processes, already outlined in Block 1 (Section 3), can operate during the migration and ultimate crystallization of magmas, and may lead to the enrichment of trace metals. These processes will be considered further in Section 2.

The operation of water as a *physical agent* involves movement of metals in the form of mineral grains in surface sedimentary environments. As a *chemical agent*, the role of water may not be so obvious, as we might not expect it to contain metals, but as revealed in Block 3, water comes from a variety of sources and can carry small concentrations of many metals in solution.

(i) *Seawater* is saline water containing 3.5% of dissolved salts and quite high levels of some major metals, but low levels of trace metals (Figure 16). It can penetrate submarine rocks through cracks and fissures, and may become trapped in marine sediments during their deposition and burial.

(ii) *Freshwater* in lakes and rivers is derived from rainfall onto land, which is therefore *meteoric water* and has a relatively low metal content. It can percolate into and travel through cracks, joints, fractures and pores in crustal rocks.

(iii) Water can be released from **hydrous minerals** (that is, minerals like the micas — Block 1, Table 7 — containing water as part of their crystal structure) when hot rocks melt but, under high pressure, it usually dissolves in the magma. If the magma rises and pressure is reduced, it is released from the magma and is known as *magmatic water*.

Beneath the Earth's surface, all kinds of water are capable of moving around under gravity and, when heated, by *convection*. Pressure due to overlying rock can also cause water to move; the resulting *compaction* of the rock and reduction of pore space leads to expulsion of pore water. These are both possible causes for the mobility of water as an agent (Figure 15).

The flow of surface water can transport metals *chemically* as ions in solution, and vigorous flow may *physically* move mineral grains. By contrast, groundwater flow is usually gentle, so is only able to transport metals in solution. Most groundwater starts out as rainwater, which is pure water except for dissolved gases and dust. However, once in the ground it passes through rock strata, and may dissolve small amounts of minerals to emerge with low concentrations of dissolved metals, as found in mineral waters (Block 3).

How can even greater amounts of metal be carried in groundwater? The solubility of metals in groundwater depends in part on the *temperature* of the water (see the box 'Solubility — variation with temperature'), in part on the nature of the other substances dissolved in the water (that is, its *composition*), and in part on the *form* in which the metals are carried. The significance of these factors will become clear as you read on.

Solubility—variation with temperature

It will be no surprise to you that most soluble substances dissolve more easily in hot water than cold. If you want to check it, take a small glass of hot water and an equal amount of cold water and see how many spoonfuls of sugar dissolve in each, roughly. When no more will dissolve, you have a **saturated solution**, which contains the maximum amount that can be dissolved under the prevailing conditions (temperature and the composition of the solution). This amount is the **solubility** of the substance at that temperature; the solubility of sugar in water increases considerably with the temperature of the solution.

Solubility is a concentration, which can be expressed as the weight of a substance per unit volume of liquid (grams per litre, $g\,l^{-1}$), or in amounts called **moles** (the amount of a substance that has the same weight in grams as its relative molecular mass*) per unit volume of liquid (moles per litre, $mol\,l^{-1}$). Although perhaps more difficult to understand, $mol\,l^{-1}$ is often easier to use. One mole of sodium chloride (NaCl) in a litre of water contains as many atoms of sodium as one mole of sodium bicarbonate ($NaHCO_3$) in a litre of water. However, the same weights of the two salts contain quite different weights of sodium, because they contain different proportions of sodium. Therefore equivalent weight concentrations of the two salts also contain different weight concentrations of sodium.

The change of solubility with temperature noted above for sugar is a general phenomenon, although the amount of change varies from one substance to another. Increasing solubility with temperature is illustrated graphically in Figure 17 for lead nitrate ($Pb(NO_3)_2$) and sodium chloride (NaCl). The solubility of lead nitrate increases considerably as temperature rises, whereas for sodium chloride there is only a small increase.

○ If you cool a hot saturated solution of a salt that is more soluble at a higher temperature than at a lower one (as in Figure 17), what will happen?

___

○ On cooling, less salt can be held in solution because its solubility at the lower temperature is less than that at the higher temperature. The excess has to go somewhere, so crystals will form. It is rather like the formation of crystals during evaporation, but that involves a decrease in the volume of water. Again, as no more salt can be accommodated in the solution beyond its solubility at saturation, the salt is forced to crystallize.

○ Use Figure 17 to calculate the weight of lead nitrate that will crystallize out of solution when $500\,cm^3$ of a saturated solution is cooled from $60\,°C$ to $20\,°C$.

___

○ At $60\,°C$ the solubility of lead nitrate is $920\,g\,l^{-1}$, so $500\,cm^3$ of saturated solution contains $460\,g$ of $Pb(NO_3)_2$. At $20\,°C$ the solubility of lead nitrate is $530\,g\,l^{-1}$, so $500\,cm^3$ of saturated solution contains $265\,g$ of $Pb(NO_3)_2$. Thus, when the solution cools from $60\,°C$ to $20\,°C$, $460\,g - 265\,g = 195\,g$ of solid $Pb(NO_3)_2$ will crystallize out.

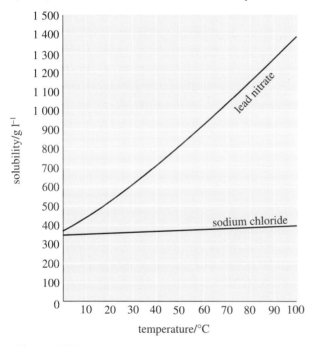

Figure 17 Variation of solubility with temperature for lead nitrate and sodium chloride.

* The relative molecular mass of a compound is the sum of the relative atomic masses of the atoms in its chemical formula.

How does the temperature variation of solubility relate to groundwaters? We know from mines and boreholes that rocks become hotter the deeper they are in the crust, so any groundwater they contain will also be hotter and therefore capable of containing higher concentrations of salts in solution. A normal geothermal gradient of $25\,°C\,km^{-1}$ will give rock and groundwater temperatures of about $160\,°C$ at a depth of $6\,km$, assuming a surface temperature of $10\,°C$.

This temperature is well above the boiling temperature of water at atmospheric pressure, but water at 6 km depth is under about 2 000 times that pressure.

○ How do you think such a pressure will affect the boiling temperature of water? (*Hint* Think about a kitchen pressure cooker.)

○ At atmospheric pressure, water boils at 100 °C, and no matter how much the water is heated its temperature will not rise; it simply turns to steam. The reason that cooking times are less in a pressure cooker is because boiling temperature is higher at increased pressure. Thus, at 6 km depth and very high pressures, the boiling temperature of water is much higher than 160 °C, and so it is still in the liquid state; it will boil to form steam only on rising to shallow depth, where the pressure is much lower.

At greater depths or in volcanic regions where rocks are hotter, groundwaters can reach even higher temperatures than this. Examples include the geothermal solutions tapped for their heat energy in the USA (Video Band 13: *Renewable Energy*). If these solutions are sufficiently rich in dissolved salts (like the lead nitrate in the example above), they may crystallize out salts on cooling. The consequences of this kind of process in ore deposit formation are the subject of Section 4.

Another factor that may affect the solubility of metals is the composition of the water, especially its acidity. For example, pure water does not attack limestone. However, rainwater is acidic because of dissolved atmospheric carbon dioxide, and gives rise to slightly acidic groundwater (containing H^+ and HCO_3^- ions) that dissolves limestone:

$$CaCO_3 + H^+ = Ca^{2+} + HCO_3^- \qquad (1.1)$$

The reaction of the groundwater with limestone reduces its acidity; in fact, it leads to an excess of OH^- ions over H^+ ions, which means that the groundwater solution becomes alkaline (see box 'The pH scale').

When rainwater is contaminated with dissolved sulphur dioxide (SO_2) and nitrogen oxides (NO_2, NO), it becomes even more acidic, and is perhaps better known as *acid rain*. Acid rain not only causes superficial deterioration of limestone buildings and carvings, but also causes damage to plants (forests) and animals (freshwater fish stocks).

At the higher temperatures and pressures of deep groundwaters, however, acidic and alkaline solutions can readily react with, or even dissolve, many minerals — not just carbonates, but silicates too. Such groundwaters are quite unlike pure water, and are called **hydrothermal fluids** (because they are watery and hot). These solutions are similar to the geothermal fluids shown in Video Band 13: *Renewable Energy*. They can be quite corrosive, and may have metal concentrations substantially greater than seawater, with as much as 25% of dissolved salts. The behaviour and composition of hydrothermal fluids will be considered further in Section 4. At this stage it is important to appreciate that they have the ability to extract or **leach** metals from a source reservoir (crustal rocks) and transport them to another location. Although their *overall* metal content may not match that of magmas, their *trace metal* concentrations may be similar. In addition, groundwater and hydrothermal fluid systems are more mobile than magmatic systems and may operate for very long periods of time — at least they don't freeze up when they penetrate cool rocks!

The pH scale

The **pH** of a solution describes how acid or alkaline it is. In fact, pH is an *inverse* measure of hydrogen ion (H⁺) concentration in solution — the *greater* the H⁺ ion concentration, the more acid is the solution and the *lower* the pH. At pH 7, the pH of *pure water*, a solution is said to be *neutral* (Figure 18), it contains equal concentrations of H⁺ and OH⁻ ions, and is neither acidic nor alkaline.

Many common liquids and natural solutions are acidic (pH < 7) and some, including seawater, are alkaline (pH > 7), as shown in Figure 18. The acidity of stomach juices may surprise you, as might the pH of lemon juice. If you have any limestone left from your Rock Kit (Block 2), see how readily lemon juice reacts with it.

The pH of most natural waters ranges from pH 4 to pH 9. Hard water, containing more OH⁻ ions than H⁺ ions, has a relatively high pH value (>7), and so is alkaline, whereas waters draining from peat bogs are acidic, having a low pH (<7), and a relatively high H⁺ concentration, because of dissolved organic acids. The acidity of waters from abandoned mine workings can be an environmental hazard and will be considered in Metals 2 — Resource Exploitation.

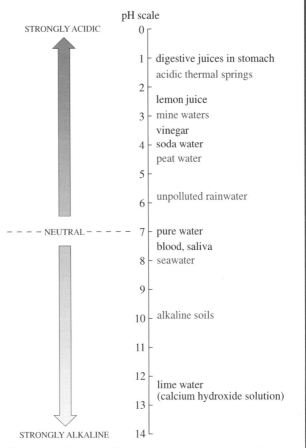

Figure 18   The pH scale, with approximate pH for common liquids and natural waters (in colour).

○ To illustrate the amount of metal that can be transported in solution over a long period of time, calculate how much calcium flows into an average home in a hard water area each year? Assume that hard tapwater contains 150 milligrams per litre (1 mg l⁻¹ = 1 ppm) of calcium ions and that the average water consumption per household is about 100 000 litres per year.

○ The weight of calcium per year = $150 \times 10^{-3} \times 10^{5}$ g = 15 kg. That's why we get furred pipes and need to descale our kettles. It shows that amounts of metals transported by large volumes of water over a long period of time can be deceptively large, even if their concentrations in solution are quite small.

Agents are capable of *transporting* ore-forming materials *only* when they are mobile. Therefore it is necessary that an agent has access to *pathways* through which it can migrate (Figure 15). Just as porous rock is of little use as an aquifer for water supply unless it is also permeable, an agent without pathways is immobile and cannot supply the metals needed to form ores. A pathway could be: a fissure that allows the flow of magma or hydrothermal fluids; a river channel that constrains the flow of surface water; or connected pores in an aquifer through which water can percolate. Perhaps the mnemonic, 'SADE', that we use to help us study ore deposit formation should really be 'SPADE', where 'P' stands for pathways. After all, what better to use, when searching for ore deposits, than a spade!

Deposition

The deposition of metals is another essential component in the formation of an ore deposit. Geochemical reservoirs, the sources of metals, are present in one form or another almost everywhere. Agents, required to remove and transport metals, must be available and able to migrate, but neither is sufficient to produce an ore deposit without a suitable *site for deposition* and, at the same time, suitable *conditions for deposition* where a change in the conditions of transportation, physical or chemical, cause ore minerals to be deposited as shown in Figure 15.

In a magma, deposition of minerals may occur within a magma chamber or in offshoots from it, and is controlled mainly by crystallization of minerals on cooling, by movement of the magma and separation of crystals (Block 1, Section 3.6). These circumstances will be considered in the discussion of magmatic ore deposit formation in Section 2.

In surface waters, a change in physical conditions, such as rates of flow, may cause deposition of mineral grains, and a change of chemical conditions may lead to the precipitation of sediments. When ions transported in solution react, possibly with newly introduced ions or the surrounding rocks, or decompose under changing pressure, temperature or pH, they may form insoluble compounds, which *precipitate* from solution. An example of precipitation familiar to many of us is the formation of scum when using soap in hard water. Most soaps are made of sodium stearate (a salt of an organic acid), which, like most sodium salts, is water soluble. In hard water, stearate ions (St^-, for short) combine with calcium ions to form insoluble calcium stearate, which forms a precipitate, or scum:

$$Ca^{2+}(aq) \; + \; 2St^-(aq) \; = \; CaSt_2(s) \qquad\qquad (1.2)$$
in hard water   from soap   scum, insoluble

Here we use the notation (aq) to indicate 'in aqueous solution', and (s) to indicate 'solid' (the insoluble precipitate). In other chemical reactions, we shall use (l) to indicate 'liquid' and (g) to indicate 'gas'. This notation will help in future to distinguish soluble and insoluble compounds involved in chemical reactions.

In hot, aqueous solutions (including both groundwaters and hydrothermal fluids) containing dissolved salts, cooling often reduces their solubility and can bring about crystallization of minerals. Also, hot, saline, possibly acidic, fluids are often reactive enough to undergo chemical exchange with minerals in the rocks through which they pass and so bring about changes in the composition of the solution. Such changes in a solution's chemical composition may affect its pH and the solubility of metal ions in solution, and may therefore bring about the precipitation of new minerals.

There are other reasons why precipitation may occur, notably changes in the chemical form of metals caused by reactions involving oxidation and reduction. This subject is further explained in the box 'Oxidation and reduction, revisited'. Changes due to oxidation and reduction are especially important in natural environments for chemical reactions involving metals, such as iron, which can exist in more than one *oxidation state**. This is because the solubility of their compounds is often quite different according

---

* The oxidation state of an element in a particular compound is effectively defined by the number of electrons available for bonding. For simple ions, it is equivalent to the charge on that ion. Thus, the oxidation state of iron in the form Fe^{2+} is II and in the form Fe^{3+} it is III. Iron in these forms is referred to as iron(II) and iron(III), respectively. Other metals that exist in more than one oxidation state include, for example, copper (copper(I) and copper(II)) and manganese (manganese(II), manganese(III), manganese(IV) and manganese(VII)).

Oxidation and reduction revisited

Oxidation and reduction were explained in Block 1 (Section 1.3), in the context of the extraction of iron from its ores, as complementary effects in chemical reactions that typically involve the addition and removal of oxygen atoms. To extend the concept of oxidation and reduction to reactions that don't involve oxygen, a broader definition is used:

oxidation is the *removal* of electrons;
reduction is the *addition* of electrons.

When iron(II) is *oxidized* to iron(III), it *loses* an electron:

$$Fe^{2+} - electron = Fe^{3+} \qquad (1.3)$$

Similarly, when iron(III) is *reduced* to iron(II), it *gains* an electron:

$$Fe^{3+} + electron = Fe^{2+} \qquad (1.4)$$

When combined with oxygen, iron(III) — the oxidized state of iron — forms the oxide Fe_2O_3, and iron(II) — the reduced state of iron — forms the oxide

FeO. Clearly, Fe_2O_3 contains proportionately more oxygen than FeO. The naturally occurring iron oxide mineral haematite (Fe_2O_3) contains iron(II), and magnetite (Fe_3O_4) contains both iron(II) and iron(III) — equivalent to FeO + Fe_2O_3. By contrast, in sulphide minerals, iron occurs in the iron(II) state in both pyrrhotite (FeS) and pyrite (FeS_2)*.

One of the best-known examples of natural oxidation is rusting. In a damp atmosphere, iron (e.g. mild steel) reacts with oxygen and water to form hydrated iron(III) oxide as follows:

$$4Fe(s) + 3O_2(g) + 2H_2O(l) \longrightarrow 2Fe_2O_3.H_2O(s) \quad (1.5)$$
$$\text{iron} \qquad \text{damp atmosphere} \qquad\qquad \text{rust}$$

Oxidation reactions at the Earth's surface frequently involve oxygen because oxygen is a powerful oxidizing agent and is available in the atmosphere.

* In pyrite, sulphur is present not as S^{2-} but as the per-sulphide anion, S_2^{2-}, analogous to the peroxide ion, O_2^{2-}, in hydrogen peroxide, H_2O_2.

---

to the oxidation state of the metal; for example, iron(II) compounds are generally far more soluble than the corresponding iron(III) compounds. When changes in a solution bring about changes in the oxidizing conditions, insoluble minerals (of iron(III), for example) may be precipitated. Such mechanisms are particularly important in the formation of ore minerals from both cool, surface waters and hot, hydrothermal solutions (Sections 3 and 4).

To form an ore deposit of any significant size not only requires a large quantity of a transporting agent and conditions favourable for the precipitation of minerals, but a suitable *site for deposition* is essential (Figure 15). In a hydrothermal system, for example, crystallizing minerals need space in which to form. Such spaces may exist as pore space, the gaps between grains in a rock, or as fractures that form when rocks are broken. Additional space may be created if minerals are dissolved by the passage of hydrothermal fluids. The site of deposition determines the form of a deposit, whether *dispersed*, as might be the case in porous or highly fractured rocks, or *confined* to fractures in largely impermeable crystalline rocks — forming **mineral veins** — or to cavities, especially in limestone, where dissolution creates spaces. On the Earth's surface the form of ore deposits produced either by escaping hydrothermal fluids or by weathering and sedimentary processes is less tightly constrained.

Question 8

Why would you expect to find hydrothermal veins in brittle, impermeable rocks rather than soft, porous rocks?

Energy

Every ore-forming process, whether it occurs within the Earth or at the Earth's surface, requires a source of energy to mobilize the agent of transportation and sometimes to assist dissolution of material prior to transport and deposition (Figure 15). The energy must also be available for a sufficiently long period of time (perhaps 10^2–10^5 years) in order to produce an ore deposit.

Heat energy derived from the decay of natural radioactive isotopes within the Earth is supplied in two ways: (i) by conductive transfer, a slow process through which rock temperatures increase with depth (the geothermal gradient), to form a long-lived feature, and (ii) by convection of hot, mobile fluids — magmas or hydrothermal solutions — that have risen from hotter, deeper zones, so short-circuiting the conductive transfer of heat, and providing local, often relatively short-lived sources of heat. Not only are high temperatures of importance in assisting chemical reactions and dissolving minerals, but they also cause the movement of fluids through convection, which is often the main driving force for the transportation of metals in solution.

 What agent is most likely to be involved in ore formation at the Earth's surface, and what forms of energy are involved in its mobilization?

 At the Earth's surface, water is the main agent available to form ores. The supply and mobilization of surface water involves the water cycle, in which the Sun's energy evaporates water to form clouds, only to be returned as rain to the Earth by gravitational energy, and to flow over or into the ground before evaporating or returning to the oceans.

1.5.2 Overview of processes involved in forming ore deposits

In later Sections, where we examine ore deposits in more detail, we shall not always discuss every one of these aspects of SADE systematically, but you should be prepared to consider each type of deposit in this manner, since it is a useful aid to understanding the interplay of geological conditions and the processes by which ore deposits are formed.

For more detailed discussion, types of ore deposit will be divided as follows, into those produced by:

(i) igneous processes, which concentrate metals in magmatic systems within the Earth and form ore minerals on solidification (Section 2);

(ii) processes acting at the surface of the Earth, where cool water is the main agent of transport, and deposition concentrates metals, either through physical movement of ore mineral grains or by precipitation of minerals due to chemical changes in solution (Section 3);

(iii) hydrothermal processes, where hot water, circulating within the crust, reacts with minerals, leaches metals, and then concentrates metals by precipitation (Section 4).

The occurrence and formation of ore deposits will be examined on a broad scale in Section 5, with links to the rock cycle and to global tectonic settings.

Why do we attach so much significance to the processes of ore formation and the geology of ore deposits? Could metal resources and their role in the environment be studied without so much geological background? In reality, the geology of ore deposit formation provides an essential insight into the natural constraints on the distribution of metal resources.

Do we expect to find metal ores everywhere?...randomly?...or can we use our *knowledge* to find deposits? Can we account for the variety of different types of metal deposit and their variable occurrence? Do we understand how the geological factors that influence the form and accessibility of a deposit also affect the price of the product? Answers to many questions about availability, lifetimes, and reserves of metal resources can be resolved only through better appreciation and understanding of their geology.

Geological knowledge also assists greatly in exploration for ore deposits and the development of extraction sites — topics covered in *Metals 2 — Resource Exploitation*. In addition, observation of geological processes involved in concentrating minerals has itself led to the development of industrial processes used for concentrating ore minerals before smelting. An understanding of geological processes also enables us to predict the effects of unnatural disturbances, such as pollution, on the natural environment, and to take the most appropriate remedial action.

1.6 *Summary of Section 1*

1 The importance of metals to the industrialized world stems from the vast array of properties that they exhibit, both in their pure form and when used in combined form in alloys, chemical compounds and composite materials. The choice of a metal for a particular use depends on the suitability of its properties, its price and the availability of substitutes.

2 The metal resources industry is a dynamic system. Usefulness and perceived value create the demand that supports the price of a metal, which may place limits on potential sources. Price also depends on the accessibility of the ore and the cost of processing necessary for the metal to be extracted. Supply is ultimately constrained by the availability of a metal, and the distribution and extent of natural concentrations. Demand can be affected by substitution for or by other materials. Price, supply and demand are all affected by economic, technological and political factors.

3 Metals are derived from ores, defined as rocks containing ore minerals in sufficient quantities to be exploited economically. To be an ore mineral, a mineral must normally contain relatively high concentrations of metals in a form that can be extracted economically. Commonly, ore minerals are oxides and sulphides, from which metals can be extracted by smelting. Ore deposits are economically minable concentrations of ore minerals produced by natural geological processes.

4 Ore minerals are chemical compounds formed naturally under favourable chemical conditions when their major constituents are available. Substitution of major constituents by trace metals may produce impurities in ore minerals. Both impurities and associated minerals in ore deposits can provide valuable metals as by-products, or create costly problems for chemical processing, necessitating the provision of environmental safeguards.

5 The grade of a rock is the concentration of metal that could be extracted. The extent of an ore body is defined by the cut-off grade, the minimum grade that can be mined economically. The estimated reserves of a large, low-grade dispersed deposit vary greatly according to the cut-off grade, and therefore on economic circumstances, whereas those of a smaller, high-grade, confined deposit are defined primarily by geological constraints on the geometry of the deposit. An extensive dispersed deposit is economic to mine at lower grades than a smaller confined deposit.

6 Many metallic elements are an essential part of the natural environment, both organic and inorganic; but excessive amounts of metals and of waste released into the environment — by the metals extraction and processing industries, for example — may have harmful effects.

7   Metals are non-renewable resources, but a degree of sustainability may be achieved by continuing current trends towards increased conservation through recycling and substitution as well as improved efficiency in extraction and exploration.

8   The Earth's crust and mantle are the main *Sources* of metals; they are concentrated by igneous, aqueous and sedimentary fractionation processes to produce ore deposits.

9   *Agents* that transport metals from their source to their site of deposition include: magmas in igneous systems; cool meteoric water and seawater at the Earth's surface; and hot, reactive groundwaters — aqueous solutions better known as hydrothermal fluids — in subsurface environments. Physical transportation involves crystal grains in magmatic systems and sedimentary grains in surface waters. Chemical transportation of metals occurs in magmas, in cool surface waters, and in hydrothermal solutions.

10 *Deposition* of ore minerals takes place where space is available, on and beneath the Earth's surface, due to changes in the physical or chemical conditions experienced by the transporting agent.

11 Forms of *Energy* involved in concentration processes include radioactive heating within the Earth, the Earth's gravitational energy and the Sun's energy at the Earth's surface. They are responsible for mobilizing the agents of transportation and promoting chemical reactions.

12 Concentration processes must operate on a large scale or for a long period of time for ore minerals to be concentrated sufficiently to form an ore deposit. This requires an ample supply of metals, a plentiful and/or long-lived supply of the agent with access to open pathways, a continuing source of energy to maintain the system, and the presence of persistent conditions with open space at the site of deposition.

2 ORE DEPOSITS FORMED BY IGNEOUS PROCESSES

Volcanoes are the most striking products of igneous processes; they are noted for their spectacular fountains of fiery lava and potentially devastating ash clouds. They are the result of magma escaping at the Earth's surface, where it cools rapidly so that igneous fractionation processes (also known as *differentiation processes*) rarely have a chance to operate or ore deposits to form. However, many igneous rocks form when magma cools and solidifies *within* the Earth, where igneous fractionation processes have a greater opportunity to operate. The nature of igneous rocks and some of the fractionation processes that accompany their crystallization were discussed in Block 1, Sections 3.5 and 3.6. Here, we shall briefly review the main magmatic processes, the igneous rocks involved, and the settings in which they occur, before looking at the ways these processes might produce ore deposits.

Magma is produced deep down in the Earth, wherever mantle or crustal rocks become so hot that they melt (Figure 19). A rock does not melt all at once, because its constituent minerals melt at different temperatures. As a rock heats up, quartz and feldspars melt first, then the micas, before amphiboles, pyroxenes and olivines (depending on which minerals are present). The result is usually a partial melt, a magma, which, being both mobile and buoyant (tending to rise, because of lower density than surrounding rocks), may separate from its source and rise through overlying rocks (Figure 19). If the magma reaches the surface, it cools rapidly to crystallize as fine-grained volcanic rock. Often, it first accumulates at depth in **magma chambers**, and if it stays there it cools slowly to crystallize as coarse-grained plutonic rock. During periods of slow crystallization in a magma chamber, physical separation of crystals and liquids of different chemical compositions

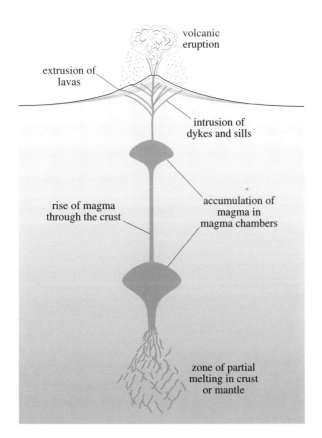

Figure 19 Basic form of a magmatic system from partial melting of source rocks to intrusion of magma to form intrusive/plutonic rocks and eruption of magma to form extrusive/volcanic rocks. The increase in temperature with depth is indicated by the increase in intensity of colour tone.

may occur. These are magmatic fractionation processes, such as fractional crystallization (Block 1, Section 3.6.1), which not only bring about changes to magma compositions, but can concentrate ore minerals to form ore deposits.

Where do magmas come from?

The origins of igneous rocks are frequently complex. They are the subject of intensive research. In detail, their magma sources and their manner of formation are often difficult to determine precisely. In general terms, however, we can recognize the processes involved in forming the main magma types and the global settings in which they are found.

(a)

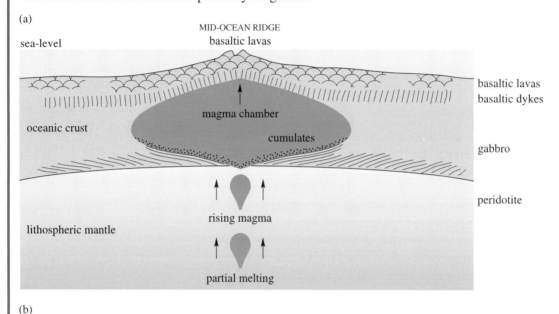

(b)

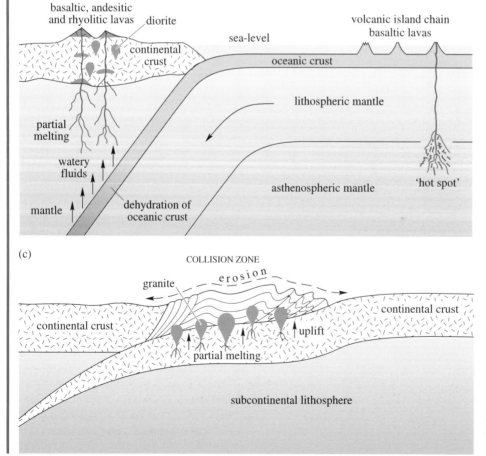

(c)

Figure 20 Sites of magma generation: (a) basaltic magma generation by partial melting of the mantle at a constructive plate margin; (b) basalt–andesite–rhyolite magma generation by water-assisted (wet) melting of mantle and crust at a destructive plate margin; basaltic magma generation at mantle 'hot spots' to form volcanic chains in ocean basins; (c) granitic magma generation by partial melting within thickened and rising continental crust of a collision zone.

Basaltic (gabbroic) magmas are derived by partial melting of peridotite mantle at high temperatures, which takes place in the following settings:

- at constructive plate margins beneath mid-ocean ridges where sea-floor spreading is active and the rising mantle partially melts (Figure 20a);

- at locations within tectonic plates where mantle partially melts beneath the lithosphere at a so-called 'hot spot', which can produce a volcanic island chain as an oceanic plate moves across it, such as the Hawaiian Islands (Figure 20b);

- at subduction zones, where cool oceanic crust heats up on descent into the mantle, hydrous minerals are dehydrated and water is driven off, leading to partial (wet) melting of the overlying mantle (Figure 20b).

Granitic (rhyolitic) magmas are formed mainly by partial melting of crustal rocks in two ways: during collision between continental masses, when the crust is thickened, and partial melting of the deeply buried crust occurs, especially on uplift, when hot rocks rise to shallow depths (Figure 20c); alternatively, crustal rocks melt when hot basaltic magmas are intruded into them, especially above subduction zones (Figure 20b) and continental 'hot spots' analogous to the oceanic 'hot spot' of Figure 20b.

Dioritic (andesitic) magmas are formed by a complex series of processes, usually involving the mixing of hot, wet, basaltic magmas and the partial melts they create on intruding and melting the crust above subduction zones (Figure 20b).

Magmatic processes take place in a number of different tectonic settings, as demonstrated in the box 'Where do magmas come from?'. They involve several different magma types, which crystallize to produce igneous rocks, the more common of which you may know already. In Block 1 you came across the rock **peridotite**, which is the main constituent of the Earth's mantle. It lies at one end of the compositional range of igneous rocks shown in Figure 21a, and comprises mainly olivine, with some pyroxene and plagioclase feldspar. At the other end of the compositional spectrum is granite, a common rock of the continental crust, useful as a building stone (Block 2, Section 2) because of its availability and durability, and when polished, attractive for its contrasting, often colourful minerals — feldspars, micas and quartz. **Gabbro** is a type of igneous rock that you may not have met. It is a coarsely crystalline rock, the plutonic (intrusive) equivalent of the volcanic (extrusive) rock, basalt, and it forms much of the Earth's crust in oceanic regions.

(a) Mineral composition

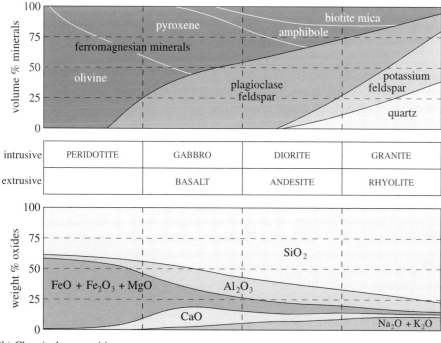

(b) Chemical composition

Figure 21 (a) Simplified mineral composition of common igneous rocks; (b) simplified chemical composition of the corresponding igneous rock and magma types.

○ What is the mineralogy of gabbro, as shown in Figure 21a?

○ It contains mainly plagioclase feldspar and ferromagnesian minerals, in roughly equal proportions.

Diorite is intermediate in composition between gabbro and granite (Figure 21a). It is also a plutonic rock, often formed within volcanic arcs (that is, oceanic island arcs and active continental margins) above subduction zones, where lavas called andesites, with a composition similar to diorite, are erupted at the surface (Figure 20). The volcanic rock with a composition similar to granite is called rhyolite. Figure 21a also shows that the mineral contents of common igneous rocks vary gradually and continuously from one rock type to another. Although most igneous rock types are defined on the basis of their mineral contents or chemical compositions, there are no abrupt compositional divisions between them.

To classify a magma, strictly we have to refer to its chemical composition, because it is molten, and not composed of minerals until it crystallizes. In practice we name it after the rock (intrusive or extrusive) that it would form on crystallization. Concentrations of chemical constituents vary continuously across the spectrum of common igneous rock types as shown in Figure 21b; this is the reason for the continuous variation in mineral contents in Figure 21a.

A comparison between mineralogical and chemical compositions in Figure 21 demonstrates a clear distinction between the *mineral* 'quartz', a particular crystalline form of pure silica, and the *chemical constituent* 'silica' (SiO_2), a term that we also use for material of that composition which may or may not be crystalline. Quartz occurs in most granitic and some dioritic igneous rocks, most sandstone and metamorphic rocks, but silica is present as a chemical component in *all* silicate rocks and minerals.

Question 9

How do concentrations of the following constituents vary from peridotite to granitic rock compositions in Figure 21?

(a) FeO, Fe_2O_3 and MgO — important constituents of ferromagnesian minerals;

(b) Na_2O and K_2O — important constituents of feldspars;

(c) silica (SiO_2) — a constituent of all silicate minerals and quartz.

2.1 Concentration of metals by magmatic processes

This Section aims to consolidate and expand your understanding of magmatic concentration processes to help you understand better how different types of magmatic ore deposits are formed.

2.1.1 Fractional crystallization

When magma cools slowly, its solidification does not happen all at once. Minerals crystallize in sequence as the temperature falls. Generally, ferro-magnesian minerals crystallize first; feldspars and quartz later. Figure 22 shows in a little more detail what happens and how the actual sequence of minerals crystallizing (Figure 22b — horizontal bars) depends on the initial magma type (Figure 22a) and its composition. Of the ferromagnesian minerals, olivine usually crystallizes before pyroxene in basaltic magmas; pyroxene is first to crystallize in dioritic magmas; and amphibole and/ or biotite mica crystallize first in granitic magmas. As temperature falls, feldspars are next to crystallize; usually the more calcium-rich varieties of plagioclase feldspar in basaltic and dioritic magmas and either the more sodium-rich varieties of plagioclase feldspar or potassium-rich alkali feldspar in granitic magmas. These patterns of crystallization are illustrated in Figure 22b.

(a) magma crystallization

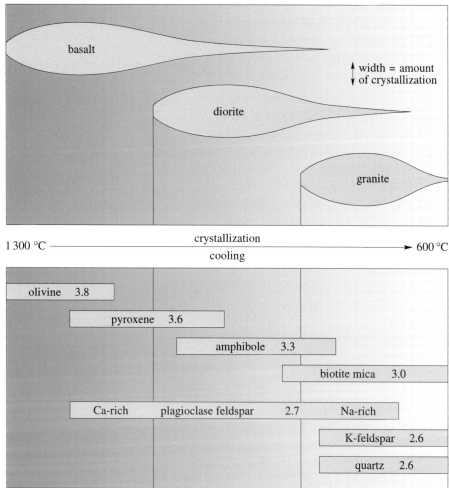

(b) order of mineral crystallization

Figure 22 Crystallization in the common magma types: (a) generalized crystallization intervals for basaltic, dioritic and granitic magmas; (b) generalized crystallization sequence of the main minerals in igneous rocks. Temperature decreases from left to right across the whole diagram and crystallization proceeds from left to right on cooling, for each magma type. In (a) the thickness of a magma envelope at a particular temperature reflects the amount of the corresponding minerals (vertically beneath) in (b) crystallizing at that temperature. Approximate densities of minerals in $t\,m^{-3}$ are given within the mineral crystallization bars (b).

○ Examine Figure 22 to decide from which types of magma quartz would crystallize.

○ Look for the magma envelopes in (a) that overlap the crystallization range of quartz in (b). Thus, quartz rarely crystallizes from basaltic magmas; it crystallizes during the later stages of crystallization of a dioritic magma, but it is one of the main minerals crystallizing from a granitic magma.

Let's consider the crystallization of a basaltic magma. Before crystallization is well advanced, mineral grains and melt can move independently. It is clear from Figure 22 that the densities of the early-crystallizing minerals, olivine and pyroxene, are significantly greater than $2.9\,t\,m^{-3}$, which is the density of basaltic magma. Figure 22 also shows that basaltic magmas are very hot. This makes them very mobile, allowing crystals of dense minerals to sink under gravity to the base of a magma chamber and form layers of rock rich in ferromagnesian minerals and therefore of different composition from the original magma. After solidification, this magma chamber would be known as a **layered intrusion**, in which the layers of accumulated minerals form **cumulate rocks**. The process involved is *fractional crystallization* (Block 1, Section 3.6.1), a form of magmatic differentiation that clearly has great potential for concentrating elements and could be exactly what is needed to form an ore deposit. But how?

Cumulate layers of ferromagnesian minerals, such as olivine and pyroxene, formed from basaltic magmas, are rich in iron and magnesium, but these metals are 'locked' in silicate minerals, from which they would be difficult and expensive to extract. Non-silicate minerals, which also crystallize from hot basaltic magmas *and* are very dense, include ilmenite ($FeTiO_3$, density $4.7\,t\,m^{-3}$), magnetite (Fe_3O_4, density $5.2\,t\,m^{-3}$) and chromite ($(Fe,Mg)Cr_2O_4$, density $5.1\,t\,m^{-3}$). They are more useful as ore minerals because they contain much higher concentrations of metals, and the metals can be more readily extracted than from silicate minerals. Normally, these oxides are found only as accessory minerals (at <1%) in igneous rocks, but in suitable circumstances in basaltic magmas they can settle to form cumulate layers sufficiently rich to be classified as ore deposits. Because of their origin, such deposits are called **magmatic segregation deposits** (Section 2.2).

○ Crystal settling is an important magmatic differentiation process, which can produce magmatic segregation deposits. What properties of the magma and crystals allow it to operate most efficiently?

○ There needs to be a *large density contrast* between the crystals and the magma, *and* the magma needs to be *very mobile* so that the crystals can sink easily.

The reason that basaltic magma is very mobile is not simply that it is very hot — much hotter than granitic magma (Figure 22) — but because its silica content is relatively low (Figure 21). The silica content of a magma exerts a strong control over its mobility: a high silica content makes it viscous (slow-moving). Granitic magmas are not only cooler but have a much higher silica content, which makes them very viscous.

○ Would fractional crystallization by gravity settling be more likely to occur in granitic or basaltic magma?

○ Gravity settling is most efficient in hot, basaltic magmas because they are very mobile and crystallize ferromagnesian minerals such as olivine and pyroxene, which are dense enough to settle under gravity. Granitic magmas are more viscous, so it would be more difficult even for dense minerals to settle. Furthermore, the minerals crystallizing from granitic magmas are not as dense as those crystallizing from basaltic ones (Figure 22), making gravity settling even less likely.

This is not to say that fractional crystallization cannot take place in granitic magmas; it can, but in other ways. In granitic magmas, fractional crystallization is likely to occur by a process called *side-wall crystallization*, whereby early-formed crystals (plagioclase feldspar, amphibole, biotite mica) form at the sides of the magma chamber as it cools. The magma close to the crystals thus loses its denser, early-crystallizing components, becomes lighter, and convects upwards. As convecting magma rises to the top of the magma chamber, the side-wall crystallization process continues to operate on it, causing its silica content to progressively increase and its ferromagnesian constituents to decrease; hence it becomes more and more granitic.

In Block 1 it was stated that, in principle, granitic magma could be derived from basaltic rock by magmatic differentiation processes. Although that is true, it would require a large proportion of cumulate minerals to separate first, so only small volumes of granite can be formed in this way. Granites are more often formed as described in the box 'Where do magmas come from?', by melting of crustal rocks. The differentiation of a *crystallizing magma* or of a *melting rock*, whichever mechanism is involved, produces *a melt richer in silica* than the starting material, and *a crystal-rich cumulate poorer in silica*. Thus, a dioritic magma could differentiate into separate portions: a granitic magma and gabbroic cumulate layers.

Because the compositions of igneous rocks produced by differentiation depend on the separation of silicate minerals from silicate melts — and are themselves formed by the melting of minerals — there are strong natural constraints on the composition of the resulting igneous rocks. Indeed this is broadly what constrains the typical major element compositions of the common igneous rock types shown in Figure 21b. However, trace element compositions are more variable than those of major elements because they are not linked so closely to the compositions of major minerals; they can either substitute in major minerals, or, if sufficiently concentrated (at high trace element abundances), form accessory minerals — minerals such as zircon and apatite (Block 1, Table 7), which are present in small amounts in many igneous rocks. Nevertheless, we can generalize about the trace element compositions of the main magma (rock) types, and give some typical abundances of selected trace metals in Table 10.

Table 10 Typical abundances of some trace elements in a range of common intrusive igneous rocks

Trace metal abundances	Peridotite/ ppm	Gabbro/ ppm	Diorite/ ppm	Granite/ ppm	Igneous rock type with greatest abundance	Average minimum exploitable grade/ppm	Minimum concentration factor
chromium, Cr	2 000	200	30	10		300 000	
copper, Cu	20	70	50	10	gabbro	5 000	
lithium, Li	0.5	10	22	40		20 000	
nickel, Ni	2 000	130	30	5		10 000	
niobium, Nb	5	15	25	40	granite	1 000	
platinum, Pt	0.05	0.01	0.005	0.001	peridotite	5	100
tantalum, Ta	0.25	0.75	1.5	2.5		500	200
tin, Sn	0.5	1.5	2	3.5		5 000	1 430
titanium, Ti	5	10 000	5 000	1 000	gabbro	30 000	3
tungsten, W	0.5	1.0	1.5	2.0		5 000	
uranium, U	0.005	1	2	3.5	granite	350	100
vanadium, V	60	400	100	30		20 000	

Question 10

Table 10 lists typical abundances of the ore-forming trace metals that occur in igneous rocks. Ore deposits are likely to be associated with the rock type in which the metal is most *abundant*. For each metal where there is a gap in the rock type column, insert the appropriate rock type. Then, for the missing minimum concentration factors, calculate the degree of concentration required to increase element abundances in the rock types selected in order to reach the average minimum exploitable grade. Examples are given to help you.

When fractional crystallization occurs, the formation of cumulate layers on the floors or side walls of magma chambers is not the only form of enrichment that occurs. The remaining liquid itself becomes enriched in constituents that are not removed by the crystallizing cumulate minerals. Therefore, some trace elements, which neither enter the structures of early-crystallizing minerals, nor form high-temperature accessory minerals such as chromite, become increasingly concentrated in the diminishing amount of melt remaining. These are known as *incompatible elements* (Block 1, Section 3.6.1) because their ionic size and charge are unsuitable for them to substitute into common silicate minerals.

● Which magma (rock) types in Table 10 could be formed by differentiation of another?

○ Magma types to the right can be formed by differentiation of those to the left. (Magmas of peridotite composition do not normally occur.)

● Which elements in Table 10 may be called incompatible?

○ Lithium, niobium, tin, tantalum, tungsten and uranium become enriched from gabbro to diorite and diorite to granite compositions and are therefore incompatible.

Most of these incompatible metals form ions with high charges, and lithium forms a small ion with a single charge, so they do not readily substitute for major elements (see Figure 7) in silicate minerals. When sufficiently concentrated (though still at trace abundances) in granitic magmas, incompatible elements may form accessory minerals, such as cassiterite (SnO_2), zircon ($ZrSiO_4$), uraninite (UO_2) and thorite ($ThSiO_4$). Highly differentiated granitic magmas, rich in incompatible metals, such as Li, Nb, Sn, Ta, W and U, may form **pegmatite deposits** (Section 2.3).

Elements that behave in the opposite manner to incompatible elements, in that they readily enter the structures of early-crystallizing minerals and are depleted in the remaining melt, are called **compatible elements**.

● Which elements in Table 10 may be called compatible?

○ Chromium, nickel and platinum are compatible elements, which are enriched in peridotite compared with gabbro, gabbro compared with diorite, and diorite compared with granite. As they enter early-crystallizing minerals that settle in basaltic magmas, they tend to be enriched in cumulate layers.

2.1.2 Separation of aqueous fluid

Volcanoes emit gases as well as lava and ash. In fact it is the build-up and release of gases dissolved in the magma that provides the energy for the most explosive volcanic eruptions. These gases include carbon dioxide (CO_2), sulphur dioxide (SO_2), hydrogen chloride (HCl) and hydrogen fluoride (HF), but usually steam (H_2O) predominates.

Deep within the Earth, water occurs mainly in hydrous minerals, such as micas and amphiboles, which contain the hydroxyl group (OH) in their crystal structure (Block 1, Table 7). Most of this water was initially acquired when low-temperature hydrous clay minerals were formed at the Earth's surface, either by weathering or by reaction between seawater and rocks of the ocean floor. During subsequent burial they are converted by metamorphism to other hydrous minerals such as micas and amphiboles, which are stable at higher temperatures. When dehydration or melting of these hydrous minerals occurs deep in the crust or mantle, the chemically bound water and other volatile products are released. At depth, under great pressure, they readily dissolve in magma.

○ At what site of magma production (in box 'Where do magmas come from?') are wet magmas likely to form?

○ In the mantle above subduction zones (Figure 20b). As cool oceanic crust heats up on descending into hot mantle, water derived from hydrous minerals is driven off and rises into the mantle of the overlying lithospheric plate. The hydrous conditions assist partial melting, and the water dissolves in the magma produced.

When wet magma containing 2–5% water rises and cools, it starts to crystallize. However, most of the minerals that crystallize at high temperatures (Figure 22) are *anhydrous minerals* (without combined water) and therefore the magma itself gradually becomes enriched in water. As crystallization proceeds, more and more water becomes concentrated into less and less magma. Eventually the magma remaining cannot accommodate any more water — it is *saturated* in water — and further enrichment will cause *magmatic water* to separate as 'bubbles', from the magma (Figure 23a). Just like bubbles of gas in water, bubbles of water in the denser magma will tend to rise and accumulate at the top of the magma chamber (Figure 23b).

Figure 23 Schematic diagrams, showing stages in the emplacement of a wet magma body as it rises to high levels in the crust: (a) as wet magma cools, it starts to crystallize, and becomes saturated with water, which separates out as 'bubbles'; (b) water scavenges soluble metals, and accumulates near the top of the magma chamber; (c) as the ascent through the crust continues, the reduction in pressure causes the water to boil, and formation of steam (occupying a much larger volume) causes explosive fracturing, forming pathways for the escaping metal-rich fluids.

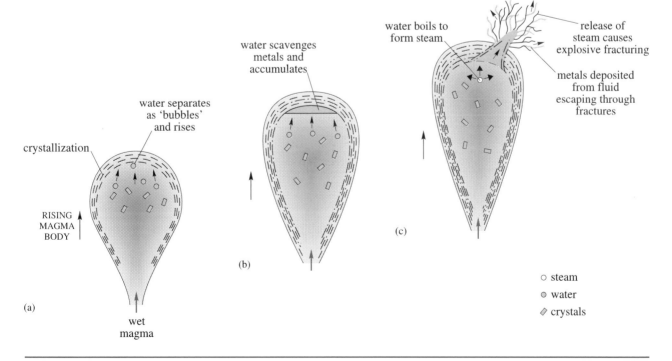

Whereas compatible elements tend to substitute into crystallizing minerals, and incompatible elements tend to stay in the magma, some metals prefer to reside not in the magma, but as ions in the separated water. Indeed, as indicated in Section 1.5, hot water can accommodate high concentrations of alkali metals. In addition to the dissolved metal ions, the water also contains other 'volatile' constituents, such as HF, HCl and CO_2. This magmatic aqueous fluid can also extract substantial amounts of trace metals from the magma, a process often called **scavenging**, which is important for the enrichment of metals in the fluid. If this reactive solution escapes into parts of a pluton in which minerals have already crystallized, or even into surrounding rocks, it may react with minerals there. The effect on the rocks and minerals with which it comes into contact is known as **alteration**, a two-way process of chemical exchange between a rock and a fluid, which necessarily also alters the composition of the fluid itself, and its ability to hold metals in solution. Such magmatic aqueous fluids are a form of hydrothermal fluid (Section 1.5).

When wet magmas reach a high level in the crust overlying subduction zones, the reduction in pressure can cause boiling of the aqueous fluid that has separated from the magma, to form steam. In addition, water still dissolved in the magma may turn directly, even explosively, to steam (Figure 23c). This is rather like the carbon dioxide bubbles that appear in lemonade when the bottle cap is unscrewed and pressure released. If the bottle is shaken first, releasing the cap can be a truly explosive experience! Such explosive events in rising magma may result in extensive fracturing of surrounding rocks and can be particularly important in creating pathways for the escape of metal-rich fluids (Figure 23c). This is an important step in the formation of **porphyry ore deposits** (to be described in Section 2.4).

2.2 Magmatic segregation deposits

As we have already seen, dense, early-crystallizing minerals can settle out in hot, basaltic magma systems to form cumulate rocks. Cumulate layers of olivine, pyroxene and plagioclase feldspar form peridotites and gabbros (Figure 21), which are generally rich in iron and magnesium, but are not in themselves ore deposits. Let's now see how essentially the same processes of fractional crystallization and the formation of cumulate layers can produce ore deposits.

2.2.1 Deposits formed by fractional crystallization

The main chromium ore mineral, chromite $((Fe,Mg)Cr_2O_4)$, is dense and crystallizes early at high temperature from basaltic/gabbroic magmas, often at the same time as olivine. Indeed, the concentration of chromium in cumulate peridotites is ten times that in gabbros (Table 10). However, to exceed the cut-off grade for chromite ore (30% Cr), further enrichment by a factor of 150 is needed (Table 10). How can this occur? Several possible explanations have been put forward. In view of its simplicity, *differential crystal settling* is still attractive. It depends on the density of chromite ($4.6\,t\,m^{-3}$) being greater than that of olivine ($3.8\,t\,m^{-3}$). If the magma convects — which is not unusual when a large body of hot, mobile liquid cools from the top — the motion may be sufficient to keep the lighter, silicate minerals in suspension, allowing only the denser chromite grains to settle and form a relatively pure layer of chromite (Figure 24a). As the magma cools, the rate of convection slows, allowing the lighter silicate minerals to settle and form a silicate-rich layer (Figure 24b).

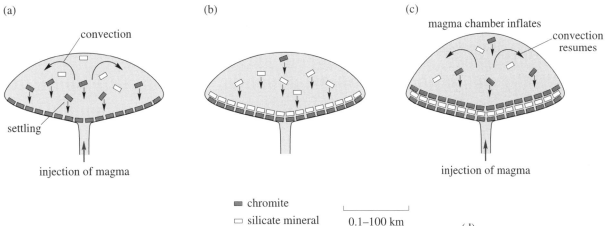

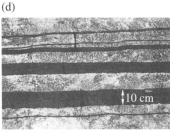

(d)

A chromite deposit, however, comprises a layered sequence of chromite, alternating with silicate minerals, as illustrated in Figure 24d. This requires the differential settling process to operate repeatedly. Such conditions could be produced by *injection of successive magma pulses* into the magma chamber, which periodically replenishes supplies of chromium and iron, and raises the magma temperature, hence increasing the rate of convection again (Figure 24c). Although zones rich in chromite layers rarely exceed a few metres in thickness, single layers can sometimes be traced laterally for a kilometre or more.

Figure 24 The formation of layered chromite deposits.
(a) A chromite layer forms at the base of a convecting magma body by crystal settling.
(b) Settling of silicate minerals forms silicate layers when convection slackens. (c) Repeated injection of magma replenishes supplies and renews convection.
(d) Alternating layers of chromite and silicate minerals in a layered complex.

The largest chromite deposits of this kind are known as **stratiform chromite deposits**; they occur in extremely large, layered igneous complexes, tens to hundreds of kilometres across and several kilometres thick, of basalt to peridotite composition. Throughout the world, there are only a few of these deposits, of which the best known are the Bushveld Complex of southern Africa (by far the largest — see the case study box), the Great Dyke of Zimbabwe, and the Stillwater Complex of Montana, USA. These enormous igneous bodies were intruded into *stable continental crust* in Precambrian times. In all of them, cumulate layers extend over very large areas, and reserves of chromite amount to *billions of tonnes*. They contrast in size with much smaller **podiform chromite deposits**, which occur as discontinuous, lens-shaped (hence the name 'podiform') bodies, individually never exceeding a *few million tonnes* of chromite reserves. Although formed by the same kind of magmatic processes as stratiform deposits, podiform deposits occur within ophiolite complexes (Block 1, Section 3.6.4), slices of oceanic crust emplaced tectonically onto continental crust often as a result of plate collision events. Small, podiform chromite deposits are more common and more widely distributed world wide than the stratiform deposits. Examples include the Vourinos Complex in Greece and Zhob valley ophiolite in Pakistan; major deposits also occur in the Urals, the Philippines and Turkey.

Although 98% of the world's chromite *reserves* are in stratiform deposits, this kind of deposit accounts for only half the world's present *production*. How would you explain this observation?

Levels of production depend mainly on *economic* factors, whereas levels of reserves depend mainly on *geological* factors. So it would be surprising if the levels of production of any mineral were closely matched to its reserves; but chromite deposits provide a particularly stark contrast. Stratiform chromite deposits are very large (especially the Bushveld) and contain vast reserves, but there are few of them. Far more podiform deposits are being worked all over the world because it is often economically more favourable for a country to mine its own deposits, however small, rather than import supplies from other countries.

2.2.2 Deposits formed by liquid immiscibility

Copper and nickel sulphides, rather like chromite, also form stratiform deposits in large igneous intrusions, such as the Sudbury Complex in Ontario, Canada. The Sudbury deposits are especially famous because it is thought likely that the magmatism was caused about 1 850 Ma ago by a meteorite impact. However, the way stratiform sulphide deposits form differs significantly from chromite deposits. The reason for this is that in basaltic magmas, *sulphide minerals crystallize at lower temperatures than most oxide and silicate minerals*. Hence sulphide crystals do not have the opportunity to sink through fluid magma to form cumulate layers as early-formed minerals do; crystallizing sulphides could only occupy spaces between other mineral grains. Consequently, *crystal* settling *cannot* produce stratiform sulphide deposits; another mechanism must operate.

Some basaltic magmas, that are particularly rich in sulphur, become *saturated* in sulphur on cooling, so that sulphur cannot be held any longer in 'solution'. Just as a separate aqueous liquid forms when 'wet' magmas become saturated (Section 2.1.1), a separate liquid is formed, a melt—not of sulphur—but of *sulphide*. It is mainly iron sulphide, because iron is the dominant metal available with sufficiently high electronegativity to combine with sulphur in basaltic magma. Only a small proportion of this sulphide remains dissolved in the silicate magma; the remainder separates from it. The sulphide liquid is said to be *immiscible* with the magma—an example of a phenomenon known as **liquid immiscibility**, which you may have noticed in gravy when globules of *fatty liquid* separate and coalesce to form a layer that floats on top of the *aqueous liquid*.

● Unlike water or fatty liquids, the iron sulphide liquid is much denser than the magma, so how does it behave on separation?

● Just as with crystal settling, the dense sulphide liquid sinks and accumulates on the floor of the magma chamber; separated water, on the other hand, would float to the top (as does oil in water).

But in contrast to crystal settling, globules of the dense liquid do not remain separate but coalesce on the floor of the magma chamber and displace the lighter magma. This is analogous to the model illustrated in Figure 25a, where snooker balls (equivalent to dense crystals) are immersed in water (equivalent to less-dense magma). When mercury (the sulphide melt), which is considerably denser than both water and snooker balls, is added, it displaces both the water and the snooker balls (Figure 25b). The snooker balls do not float on top of the mercury because the pressure of balls above (that sink in the water) depresses them. Similarly, a silicate melt and cumulate minerals (such as chromite and olivine) float on top of a sulphide melt, producing, on cooling and crystallization, a mixed capping of silicates set in sulphide that is often a feature of stratiform sulphide layers (Figure 25c).

Iron is the dominant metal in the sulphide melt. So, when the sulphide melt cools, it crystallizes mainly as pyrrhotite (FeS), the form of iron(II) sulphide that is stable at high temperatures. Before that, globules of molten sulphide scavenge from the magma those *more highly electronegative metals* that have affinities for sulphur (see 'Electronegativity' box and Figure 6a in Section 1.2).

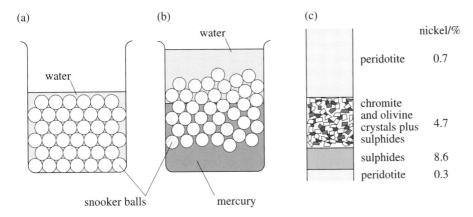

Figure 25 The snooker ball model illustrating the concentration of sulphide melt by liquid immiscibility and gravity settling towards the base of a magma chamber: (a) snooker balls (crystals) immersed in water (magma); (b) when the dense liquid mercury (the sulphide melt) is added, it displaces both the water and the snooker balls; (c) a schematic section (with grades of nickel) through a typical sulphide magmatic segregation deposit associated with peridotite layers (cumulate silicates) at the base of a layered basaltic intrusion.

○ Which of the more electronegative metals (values > 1.8) in Figure 6a are present at relatively high concentrations (say, more than 50 ppm) in basaltic magma (i.e. gabbro in Table 10) and thus available to be scavenged by the sulphide melt?

○ Only copper and nickel.

Copper and nickel form the sulphide minerals chalcopyrite ($CuFeS_2$) and pentlandite (($Ni,Fe)_9S_8$), respectively, on cooling and crystallization of the sulphide melt. Crystallized blobs of sulphide, mainly pyrrhotite and chalcopyrite, with minor pentlandite, are illustrated in Plate 55, a sample of sulphide-bearing ore from the Sudbury Complex. The nickel concentrations in Figure 25c reflect sulphide concentrations in a typical layered sequence. The *sulphide melt* also scavenges highly electronegative *precious metals*, such as gold and platinum. On cooling, these metals may also form sulphides, or crystallize as native metals or even metal alloys in the sulphide layers.

Formation of multiple sulphide layers is likely to be the result of the injection of successive pulses of magma, as previously indicated for multiple chromite layers. Important ore-bearing stratiform sulphide deposits of this kind occur within the Bushveld and Stillwater Complexes, where platinum ores are mined in their own right from thin sulphide-rich layers. In contrast, at Sudbury, the world's greatest source of nickel, platinum is only a by-product of copper and nickel sulphide mining.

In iron-rich magma compositions, immiscibility of an *iron oxide melt* can lead to the formation of ilmenite ($FeTiO_3$) and magnetite (Fe_3O_4) layers. Ilmenite layering is an important source of titanium, and ores of this kind, grading 30–35% TiO_2, are mined from the Lac Tio deposit at Allard Lake, Quebec, which supplies 19% of the world's titanium dioxide (TiO_2). Such deposits are not common, but there are several world wide; the largest, with reserves of 300 Mt, and grading 18% TiO_2, is at Tellness in southern Norway.

The Bushveld Complex—possibly the most valuable ore deposit in the world?

(a)

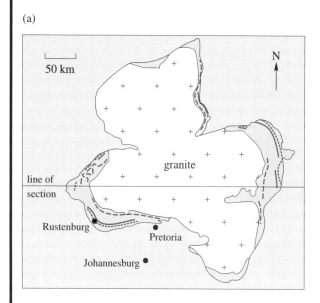

(b)

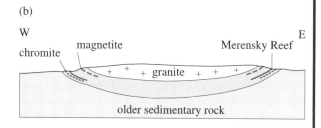

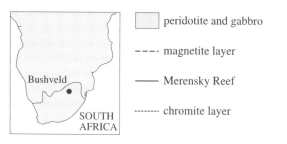

(c)

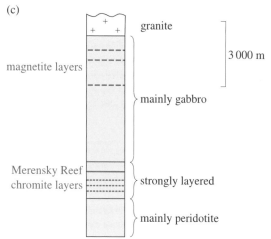

Figure 26 The Bushveld Complex: (a) plan view, showing extent of economic horizons; (b) E–W cross-section; (c) idealized vertical section through the Bushveld Complex.

are exposed only at the eastern and western margins of the Complex (Figure 26a and b).

The main chromite deposits lie within the strongly layered zone, mostly near its base, as a series of layers, a few centimetres to 2 m thick and extending laterally for many kilometres. Accessible chromite reserves shallower than 300 m amount to over 2 billion tonnes, but ten times this amount would be available if mining were extended to lower grade ores and to a depth of 1 200 m. The Bushveld Complex represents about 75% of the world's chromite reserves.

Near the top of the strongly layered zone there is a thin sheet less than 1 m thick comprising coarsely crystalline pyroxene. At its upper and lower margins are thin, centimetre-thick layers containing chromite, but also rich in sulphides, and more importantly, rich in platinum and other precious metals. This sheet is probably the best-known part of the Bushveld intrusion, and is known as the Merensky Reef (Figure 26c), after Hans Merensky, an early prospector. It is mined as a whole unit because the narrow, centi-metre-thick layers would be impossible to mine alone. The grade of platinum reaches 7.5–11 g t^{-1}, well above the cut-off grade for platinum of 5 g t^{-1}. Platinum occurs in the Merensky Reef as native metal, as a natural alloy, and also as minerals, such as sulphides, arsenides and antimonides, in association with other precious metals such as palladium, ruthenium, gold, rhodium and iridium.

What is the Bushveld Complex and why should it be one of the world's most valuable ore deposits? Firstly, it is an extremely large, saucer-shaped igneous intrusion (Figure 26b), some 300 km across and 6 to 8 km thick, underlying an area of 67 000 km^2 just north of Pretoria in South Africa (Figure 26a). Most of this huge, 1 500 billion tonne body, however, is not ore at all; overall it is of basaltic composition, differentiated into a lower part of mainly peridotite and an upper two-thirds of mainly gabbro (Figure 26c). Between these major divisions, there is a zone of strongly layered rocks with individual cumulate layers rich in pyroxene, calcium-rich plagioclase or chromite. This is the zone that is richest in chromite and platinum ores. At higher levels in the intrusion, there are layers of cumulate magnetite, important for their high vanadium content (grading 0.5–2% V$_2$O$_5$). The shape of the intrusion, and the presence of granite—formed from melted crustal material—overlying it in the middle, means that ore deposits

● Where do you find the metals palladium, ruthenium, gold, rhodium, and iridium in the Periodic Table, and why (looking back at Figure 6a) might you expect them to occur naturally with platinum?

● Iridium and gold occur on either side of platinum in the same Period of the Periodic Table, whereas palladium is in the same Group as platinum. Palladium, ruthenium, rhodium, and iridium have the same electronegativity (2.2) as platinum (Figure 6a). The consequent similarities in atomic structure and chemical properties of platinum and ruthenium, rhodium, palladium, osmium and iridium is responsible for their similar geochemical behaviour and occurrence, and is the reason for using the collective term *platinum group elements* (PGE) for them all.

The grades of copper (0.11%) and nickel (0.18%) sulphides in the Merensky Reef are much lower than in the Sudbury ores, but even these abundances are sufficient for copper and nickel to be recovered as *by-products* of PGE mining. Several hundred metres below the Merensky Reef, another platinum deposit has been discovered more recently. This is a chromite layer 0.5–2.5 m thick, with platinum grades of 3.5–19 g t^{-1}. It's likely to supply not only precious metals but also large amounts of chromite.

What then is the value of Bushveld ores? Reserves of PGE in the Bushveld are believed to exceed 60 000 tonnes, which is something like 80% of the total world reserves of these metals, and very large in comparison to the world's total annual extraction of 300 tonnes in the early 1990s. With the price of platinum around $375 per troy ounce (the normal unit for pricing precious metals; there are 32 150 troy ounces per metric tonne) or $12 050 per kilogram, perhaps the Bushveld Complex may be justifiably regarded as one of the world's most valuable deposits.

In addition, the Bushveld contains 75% of the world chromite reserves, and judging by its price (Table 4), chromium is one of the more valuable of the major metals. The vanadium-bearing magnetite layers near the top of the Bushveld intrusion, minable at thicknesses around 1.8 m, are also valuable, accounting for 50% of the world's vanadium supply. Most chromium and vanadium is not produced as pure metals, but is used in making steel alloys.

Question 11

(a) The similarities and differences between the processes that give rise to chromite-rich and PGE-rich layers in the Bushveld Complex are described in the following paragraph.

The......minerals in both the chromite-rich and PGE-rich layers are ....and form sequences of thin layers over a wide......... They formed by............settling and the repeated injection of.........pulses during crystallization of the intrusion. The............layers contain minerals that..............from the magma, whereas the Merensky Reef contains...........minerals that originally separated as an.............. melt, scavenged the more....................metals from the magma and collected some chromite crystals on settling.

To show your understanding of these processes, fill in the missing words from the list below:

area; chromite; crystallized; dense; electronegative; gravity; immiscible; magma; ore; sulphide.

(b) The reserves of PGE in the Bushveld Complex amount to 60 000 t. Assuming the reserves account for 80% of the total PGE (the remaining 20% being in non-economic parts) in the intrusion (total mass 1 500 × 10^9 t), what is the average concentration of PGE in the intrusion as a whole? This represents the composition of the initial (undifferentiated) magma. What degree of concentration has produced ores averaging 10 g t^{-1}?

2.3 Pegmatite ore deposits

In the broadest sense, **pegmatites** are very coarse-grained igneous rocks, generally of granitic composition, and composed principally of quartz, potassium feldspar and muscovite mica (see Plate 56). Pegmatite ore deposits are generally associated with granite plutons and are important for the exotic metals they contain, including beryllium, caesium, cerium, lithium, niobium, rare earth elements, rubidium, tantalum, thorium, tin, tungsten, uranium and zirconium. Several of these metals cannot be obtained from other sources, and have important, often specialized, uses, as demonstrated in Table 11. Some of the ore minerals listed in Table 11 are normally found as *accessory minerals* in granitic rocks, but only in pegmatites are they ever abundant enough to constitute ore deposits. Other minerals commonly found in pegmatites, such as topaz $(Al_2SiO_4(F,OH)_2)$, tourmaline (a borosilicate mineral) and lepidolite (a lithium mica), contain elements like fluorine and boron, which are often lost from magma as volatile compounds, such as water, hydrogen fluoride (HF) or boron trifluoride (BF_3).

Question 12

Some of the metals found in the pegmatite ore minerals listed in Table 11 also appear in Figure 7. Which are they, and how do their ionic charges and ionic radii compare to those of the major metals sodium, calcium, potassium, iron, magnesium and aluminium? What is the implication of these observations for ionic substitution in rock-forming minerals?

Some pegmatites are mined for their large crystals, many of which have important industrial uses, such as feldspar (in ceramics), quartz (in optics), fluorite (as fluxes, chemical feedstock, etc.) and sheet mica (in electronics).

Table 11 Metals concentrated in pegmatites, their minerals, uses and properties

Metal	Mineral/formula	Important uses	Important properties
beryllium, Be	beryl, $Be_3Al_2(SiO_6)_{18}$	brake discs for jet aircraft; windows for X-ray tubes	low density; high m.t.* (1 279 °C); resistance to metal fatigue; heat insulation; transparency to X-rays; toxicity
caesium, Cs	pollucite, $(Cs,Na)_2Al_2Si_4O_{12}.H_2O$	atomic clocks and light-sensitive detectors	nuclei of caesium atoms have different energy states
cerium, Ce	monazite, $CePO_4$	coatings for high-definition TV tubes; lighter flints	phosphorescence; high-friction alloy
lithium, Li	spodumene, $LiAlSi_2O_6$	low-density alloys; batteries; coolant in nuclear reactors	low density; high thermal conductivity; low m.t. (180 °C)
tantalum, Ta	tantalite, $FeTa_2O_6$	military warheads; electronic capacitors; surgical implants	high density; machinable; high resistivity; very high m.t. (2 996 °C); corrosion resistance
tin, Sn	cassiterite, SnO_2	tinplate; float glass; alloys (bronze, pewter, solder, gunmetal)	low m.t. (232 °C); corrosion resistance
tungsten, W	wolframite, $FeWO_4$	abrasive and cutting tools (tungsten carbide); high-speed steel; darts; lightbulb filaments	high density; very high m.t. ($\approx$3 400 °C); low thermal expansion
uranium, U	uraninite, UO_2 (U_3O_8)	fuel for nuclear reactors	fissile isotopes

* m.t. = melting temperature.

Figure 27, which features the lithium mineral spodumene, demonstrates just how large the crystals in a granite pegmatite can be. The potential for the *simultaneous extraction* of industrial minerals (important for the size of their crystals), as well as ore minerals of incompatible elements (Table 11), makes pegmatites attractive exploration targets. Valuable gemstones, such as topaz and aquamarine, the turquoise blue variety of beryl shown in Plate 57, are also obtained from pegmatites.

In scale, however, most pegmatite deposits are small compared with many of today's ore deposits. Some metals, such as rare earth elements and niobium, formerly obtained from pegmatites, are now more easily obtained from alternative sources (unusual igneous rocks called carbonatites). Localities still important for mining pegmatite ores include the Greenbushes Pegmatite in Western Australia, for lithium in spodumene, and the Tanco Pegmatite at Bernic Lake in Manitoba, Canada, for tantalum, lithium and niobium.

Figure 27 Gigantic spodumene crystals, over 10 metres long and up to 2 metres across, in a granite pegmatite mine. See man for scale.

Pegmatites commonly occur as lenses or sheet-like intrusions. Most pegmatites are small, but range from a few centimetres across and metres in length, to a few metres across and hundreds (occasionally thousands) of metres in length. Usually their mineralogy is simple and they are **unmineralized** (without ore minerals); less commonly they are zoned, with a regular, concentrically layered arrangement of minerals — as shown in Figure 28 — and may be **mineralized** (contain ore minerals). A zone (layer) in a pegmatite is defined by both its mineralogy and its texture, so it is possible to have different zones containing the same minerals but distinguished by variations in grain size, or mineral proportions or both. The example of a mineralized zoned pegmatite in Figure 28 features a progression from a granitic border zone inwards through more coarsely crystalline zones of quartz and potassium feldspar to a core region containing quartz, beryl, tourmaline and spodumene. Sometimes, cores contain cavities — open spaces — where crystals can grow unrestricted, to form gem-quality crystals (Plate 57).

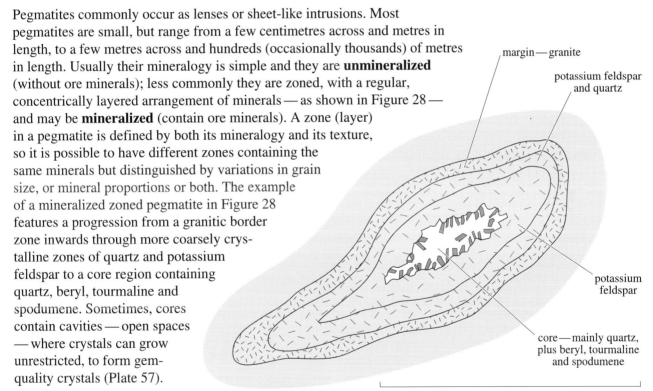

margin — granite

potassium feldspar and quartz

potassium feldspar

core — mainly quartz, plus beryl, tourmaline and spodumene

0.1 – 100 m

Figure 28 Schematic representation of the internal structure of a zoned pegmatite, showing concentric textural and mineralogical zonation. Minerals rich in incompatible elements (if present) are concentrated at the core.

⬤ How do the zones in an individual pegmatite (Figure 28) provide clues to their formation and the concentration of incompatible elements in pegmatites?

⬤ Pegmatites crystallize from the outside inwards. *Anhydrous* silicate minerals such as plagioclase feldspar, alkali feldspars and quartz form the outer zones, causing an increase in the proportion of water *and* incompatible elements in the remaining magma. Eventually, hydrous and incompatible element-bearing minerals crystallize from the enriched magma at the core of the pegmatite.

The process just described is a form of fractional crystallization, taking place *in situ* in a pegmatite magma. But how is the pegmatite magma formed? Figure 29 shows how crystallization of anhydrous (water-free) minerals from a 'normal' granitic magma with an initial water content of only 0.2% can produce melts that are progressively enriched in water. When the amount of the remaining melt halves, its water content doubles. When 97.5% of the magma has crystallized, the water content of the remaining 2.5% melt has increased 40 times to 8%. Similar enrichment of 'volatiles' (F, B, H_2O) and incompatible metals is also possible until they enter crystallizing minerals or escape in fluids.

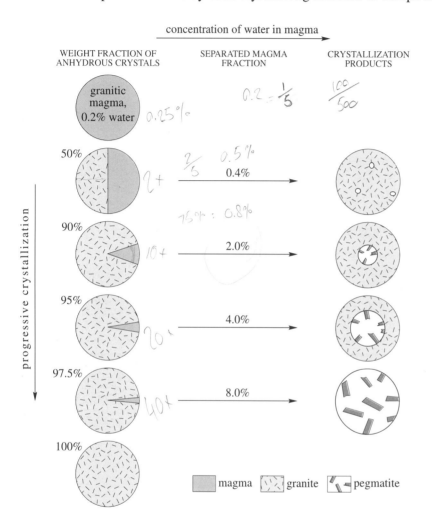

Figure 29 Formation of pegmatite from normal granitic magma by enrichment of water in the magma remaining after crystallization of anhydrous minerals. The greater the enrichment of the water in the separated magma fraction, the greater the proportion of pegmatite on crystallization.

Question 13

Use Figure 29 to estimate the concentration of lithium in the melt remaining after 97.5% crystallization of a granitic magma having an initial lithium concentration of 10 ppm. Assume that lithium behaves incompatibly, like water, and does not enter crystallizing minerals.

Experimental work has shown that a granitic magma containing high concentrations of water (over 5%) and 'volatile' incompatible elements such as fluorine and boron, has very different properties from a normal (dry) granitic magma. These constituents of a pegmatite magma have the effect of dramatically reducing both its viscosity and its temperature of crystallization, as well as promoting the formation of large crystals. In contrast with the viscous nature of a dry granitic magma, a pegmatite magma is very mobile and can migrate through available fractures in solidified granite and surrounding rocks, accounting for the sheet-like form of many pegmatites.

The Rössing uranium deposit, Namibia—energy from the desert

(a)

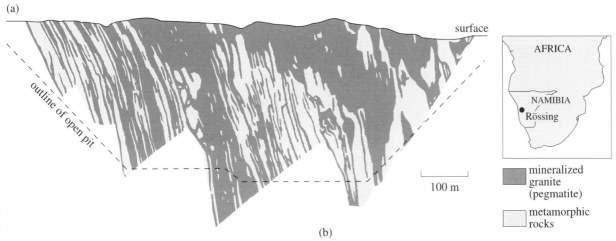

100 m

■ mineralized granite (pegmatite)

□ metamorphic rocks

(b)

One of the largest (though not the most typical) pegmatite deposits to have been exploited is the Rössing uranium deposit in the Namib Desert of Namibia, southern Africa (Figure 30). It is also the largest known deposit of uranium ore occurring in granite; it is 2.5 km long, 1 km wide, and extends to a depth of at least 0.3 km. The granitic magma was injected some 500 Ma ago into a thickened crustal zone of metamorphic rocks. Associated pegmatites contain quartz, potassium feldspar, plagioclase feldspar and small amounts of biotite mica, with dispersed concentrations of the accessory mineral, uraninite (UO_2, but sometimes quoted as U_3O_8). Although uranium ore minerals are restricted to the pegmatites, most of the pegmatites are unmineralized, some have traces of mineralization, and only a tiny proportion are sufficiently rich in uranium to be worth mining.

A cross-section through the deposit (Figure 30a) shows a complex relationship between numerous sheets of ore-bearing coarse-grained granite (the pegmatite) and the interlayered unmineralized metamorphic rocks. These relationships are clearly visible in outcrop (Figure 30b). The primary ore minerals (mainly uraninite and complex mixed oxides of U, Nb, Fe and Ti) account for about 60% of the uranium present, and are often enclosed within large crystals of quartz, mica and feldspar. The remaining 40% of the uranium has a secondary origin, having been dissolved from primary uranium minerals by groundwater and then precipitated from the uranium-bearing solution to form a bright yellow mineral, known as beta-uranophane, which replaces primary uraninite grains as well as forming thin films on fractures and grain boundaries.

The average grade of 0.031% U_3O_8 is very close to cut-off grade, but the size of the deposit and its ease

Figure 30 (a) Cross-section showing the form of the Rössing uranium deposit; (b) typical form of the granitic (pegmatitic) veins in outcrop.

of extraction (opencast pit and underground mine) have made the operation economic. Reserves have been estimated at 120 000 tonnes of uranium, which is about 5% of the world total. The decline in demand for nuclear power in the 1990s has reduced world demand and the price of uranium. As a result, the output of Rössing has been cut from about 5 000 t y^{-1} of U_3O_8 concentrate in the 1980s to 2 270 t in 1991, and to only 850 t in 1992 and 1993. Long-term agreements to buy uranium ore at guaranteed prices, now well above world averages, are responsible for continued mining of such low-grade deposits at a time when the uranium mining industry is in decline.

Internal zonation of individual pegmatites (Figure 28) represents further fractional crystallization once the pegmatite magma has reached its final destination.

Many properties of solutions are readily applicable to magmas. When particular constituents become enriched to the point of saturation, they can no longer stay in the magma and may crystallize as minerals. In water-rich magmas, water may separate as a liquid or a gas (Section 2.1.2), and escape to form a hydrothermal fluid. Loss of water from the magma causes its crystallization temperature to rise; consequently, the magma freezes rapidly and a fine-grained granitic rock called an *aplite* forms. Aplites often occur in association with pegmatites, reflecting a loss of water and, with it, soluble incompatible elements, which may subsequently form ore deposits in circumstances considered further in Section 4.3.2.

Question 14

(a) With an average grade of 0.031% U_3O_8 (equivalent to 0.026% uranium) and reserves of 120 000 t uranium, what would be the lifetime of the Rössing mine at:

   (i)   1980s extraction rates of 15 Mt y^{-1} of ore?

   (ii) early 1990s extraction rate of 2.5 Mt y^{-1} of ore?

(b) How will the future of the nuclear power industry (Block 4 Part 2) affect mining at Rössing?

2.4 Porphyry ore deposits

Porphyry is a textural term used to describe an intrusive igneous rock made up of relatively large crystals set in a matrix (or groundmass) of finer-grained crystals (Block 1, Section 3.5.1). Porphyry ore deposits acquired their name because porphyritic texture (rather like that of the Shap granite shown in Plate 1) is a distinctive feature of the plutonic igneous rocks with which they are associated. Porphyry ore deposits are large-scale, low-grade, dispersed deposits, containing varying amounts of copper, molybdenum or tin ore minerals, along with lesser amounts of gold, silver and tungsten, which are often mined as valuable by-products. None of these deposits were mined before 1905. They only became viable with the development of large-scale methods, such as powered shovels and rail track to transport rock, together with improved methods of processing and separating ore minerals. Today, porphyry deposits provide over 50% of the world's copper and 70% of the world's molybdenum; they are located mainly in the Cordilleran mountain ranges of North and South America, and the islands of the western Pacific.

The Bingham Canyon Mine in Utah, USA (near Salt Lake City), was the first porphyry copper deposit to be mined, and even today it ranks as one of the largest ore deposits in the world (Figure 31). The deposit is about 2.5 km long, 1.7 km wide and over 1 km in depth. Since Bingham opened, over a billion tonnes of ore, yielding an average of 0.9% Cu have been mined from it, and yet it still has ore reserves of 1.7 billion tonnes exceeding 0.7% Cu. Not only does this scale of extraction produce a gigantic 'crater' (in fact, the biggest man-made hole in the world, 7.2 km² in area and 800 m deep), as shown in Figure 31, but large volumes of waste which potentially generate massive environmental problems.

Figure 31 An aerial view of the Bingham Canyon open pit porphyry copper mine, Utah, which is about 2 km across.

Porphyry copper deposits are generally found in association with small, 1–2 km diameter, igneous intrusions of diorite or granodiorite composition. (As its name suggests, granodiorite is a rock type intermediate between granite and diorite.) Although pyrite (FeS_2) is the dominant sulphide mineral, the ore minerals are mainly copper sulphides, such as chalcopyrite ($CuFeS_2$) and bornite (Cu_5FeS_4), which are dispersed throughout large volumes of rock in a complex network of tiny veinlets called a **stockwork**, as featured in Plate 58. The sample shown in Figure 32a is typical of a porphyry copper stockwork ore in which intense fracturing and recrystallization have almost obliterated the original porphyritic texture of the host rock. As we shall see later, these effects have resulted from the passage of metal-bearing fluids (of the kind described in Section 2.1.2), which not only deposited small concentrations of ore minerals, but reacted with the surrounding rock, causing changes in its mineralogy, a process known as *wall-rock alteration*.

Mineralized porphyry intrusions are generally emplaced as wet, partially crystalline magmas (typically containing 3% H_2O), at shallow depth in the crust (typically 1–2 km). The reduction in pressure as the magma rises, and the increasing concentration of water in the magma due to crystallization of mainly anhydrous minerals, cause the magma to become saturated with

Figure 32 (a) Typical example of porphyry copper stockwork ore, showing mineralized veins containing copper sulphides occupying fractures, and wall-rock alteration around them, which has almost obliterated the porphyritic texture of the host rock. (b) Mineralized breccia from a breccia pipe — broken fragments of porphyritic igneous rock (light areas, mottled), cemented by a mixture of tourmaline, pyrite and chalcopyrite (dark areas); formed by explosive activity of mineralizing fluids associated with a porphyry ore deposit.

(a)

(b)

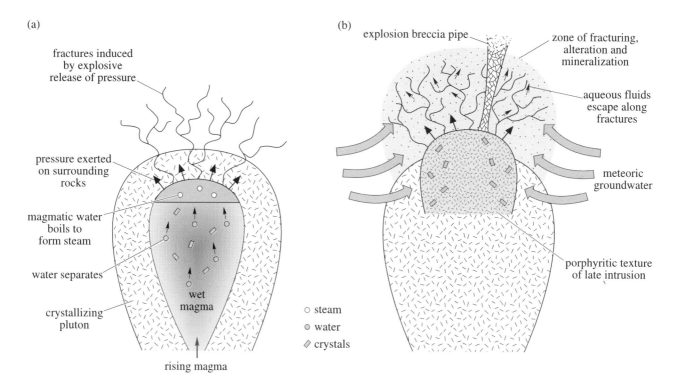

(a)

fractures induced by explosive release of pressure

pressure exerted on surrounding rocks

magmatic water boils to form steam

water separates

crystallizing pluton

wet magma

rising magma

○ steam
◉ water
⬦ crystals

(b)

explosion breccia pipe

zone of fracturing, alteration and mineralization

aqueous fluids escape along fractures

meteoric groundwater

porphyritic texture of late intrusion

water. 'Bubbles' of water then *separate* from the magma (Section 2.1.2), and rise to the top of the magma chamber (Figure 33a). Water-soluble metals, such as copper, may be *scavenged* to form a metal-rich aqueous magmatic fluid. As the magma body continues to rise, further reduction of pressure may cause this fluid to *boil*.

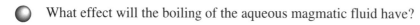

What effect will the boiling of the aqueous magmatic fluid have?

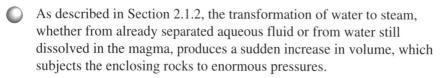

As described in Section 2.1.2, the transformation of water to steam, whether from already separated aqueous fluid or from water still dissolved in the magma, produces a sudden increase in volume, which subjects the enclosing rocks to enormous pressures.

This sudden and explosive release of pressure can make rocks shatter (Figure 33a), allowing water and steam to escape, and magma to rise further (Figure 33b). The sudden loss of water from the magma raises its crystallization temperature, causing it to crystallize more rapidly and so develop a *porphyritic texture*, with early-formed, coarse-grained crystals in a fine-grained groundmass. If the force of the explosion is extreme, gases may escape to the surface via a breccia pipe containing an *explosion breccia* of jumbled and broken rock (Figures 32b and 33b). A **breccia** is a rock composed of angular, broken rock fragments, often derived from a variety of pre-existing rock types; breccias may also be formed by sedimentary accumulation or along fault zones.

When the escaping hot, aqueous, magmatic fluids pass through newly formed fractures, they not only cool and deposit ore minerals (such as copper sulphides), but may also permeate the surrounding rock, where they react with minerals and bring about wall-rock alteration. *Repeated* boiling of magmatic water, fracturing of rock and escape of fluids (water and steam), produces a thoroughly altered and mineralized *stockwork* (Figure 32a and Plate 58). Alteration of the surrounding rocks is useful in locating porphyry mineralization because the alteration 'halo' produced by the mineralizing fluids (shown in Figure 34a) is usually distinctive and is much larger than the mineralized region itself (compare with Figure 34b).

Figure 33 The magmatic stages in the formation of a porphyry ore deposit. (a) Emplacement and crystallization of wet granodioritic magma, and separation of water, followed by boiling. This causes an explosive release of gases and build-up of pressure to produce fracturing, which allows further injection of magma. (b) Rapid crystallization of the porphyritic intrusion, formation of an explosion breccia pipe and the escape of aqueous magmatic fluids through fracture zones. Heat from the intrusion convects hydrothermal fluids derived both from the magma itself and meteoric groundwater drawn in from surrounding rocks.

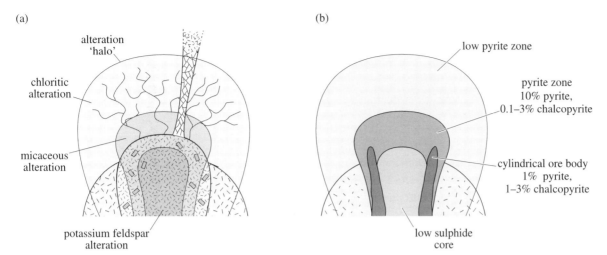

(a)

alteration 'halo'

chloritic alteration

micaceous alteration

potassium feldspar alteration

(b)

low pyrite zone

pyrite zone 10% pyrite, 0.1–3% chalcopyrite

cylindrical ore body 1% pyrite, 1–3% chalcopyrite

low sulphide core

Figure 34 Patterns of alteration and mineralization associated with porphyry ore deposits, superimposed on the porphyry intrusion featured in Figure 33, to show (a) zonation of alteration products to form a 'halo', and (b) the distribution of sulphide mineralization typical of a porphyry copper deposit.

Characteristic alteration zones (Figure 34a) include a high-temperature potassium feldspar alteration zone, centred on the porphyry intrusion, which gives way outwards to a zone of micaceous alteration and then to a lower-temperature zone, characterized by chlorite, a flakey green mineral. The ore deposit itself is usually centred on the porphyry intrusion, but not confined to it. The distribution of ore minerals is also zoned, as illustrated in Figure 34b. The most common shape for the ore body is that of a steep-walled cylinder, and outside that is a pyrite-rich zone, which extends roughly to the boundary between the zone of potassium feldspar alteration and the surrounding zone of micaceous alteration. In the zone of chloritic alteration, the mineralization is variable, but is mainly non-economic.

The intrusions that produce porphyry deposits and supply the magmatic fluids are also a source of heat. This brings about convection, which draws in and heats up *meteoric groundwaters* from surrounding rocks (grey arrows in Figure 33b). On mixing with hot *magmatic fluids* and eventually cooling, ore minerals may be deposited (by mechanisms to be discussed for hydrothermal systems in Section 4). Therefore, porphyry mineral deposits are in part produced by the interaction of different aqueous fluid systems: their early (higher temperature) mineralization is derived largely from magmatic fluids; subsequently, it is 'overprinted' with later (lower temperature) mineralization and alteration due largely to meteoric fluids.

Another process that is an important feature of many porphyry deposits (and detailed further in Section 3.2.2), occurs when erosion brings the porphyry deposit close to the surface, often *long after it formed*. This process involves leaching of primary sulphide minerals by percolating groundwater. Leached metals are then precipitated as secondary sulphide minerals to form an enriched zone of secondary mineralization at fairly shallow depth. Given the low grade of most porphyry deposits (around 0.8% Cu), localized enrichment of perhaps five to ten times this grade is often economically significant.

Porphyry molybdenum and porphyry tin deposits have many of the features (large tonnages, low-grade dispersed mineralization, alteration haloes) seen in porphyry copper deposits, although most of them are associated with intrusions of granitic rather than of granodioritic composition. Molybdenum porphyries in the western USA account for half the world's molybdenum reserves, and include the famous Climax deposit in the state of Colorado. The cut-off grade for molybdenum is about 0.1% molybdenite (usually quoted in this way because molybdenite, MoS_2, is the main molybdenum ore mineral); grades usually range from 0.1–0.5% MoS_2. Tin porphyries are known in Bolivia and Alaska, but such deposits grading 0.2–0.3% Sn (in which cassiterite, SnO_2, is the main ore mineral) are uneconomic at present.

The Chilean porphyry copper belt and Chuquicamata copper mine — the largest copper producer in the world

The Andean mountain chain has long been one of the world's most important mining areas. The Incas worked gold and silver for ornamental purposes, and made bronze weapons, well before the Spanish invaded. The Andes lie along the western margin of the South American continent, under which the oceanic Nazca Plate is being subducted (Figure 35a). This *destructive plate margin* is consequently a region of intense seismic and volcanic activity.

Many ore deposits within the Andes are related to igneous intrusions of dioritic or granodioritic composition of Cretaceous–Tertiary age. Porphyry copper deposits in the Western Cordillera are the most important economically, but related hydrothermal vein deposits contain lead, zinc, copper and silver. In the Eastern Cordillera, porphyry and vein deposits contain tin, tungsten and silver. Bolivia is a leading exporter of tin, and mining of porphyry copper deposits has made Chile the world's leading copper producer. In 1992, Chile not only produced 2 Mt of copper, but also 15 000 t of molybdenum, 224 000 kg of silver and 2 200 kg of gold, largely as by-products of porphyry copper mining.

Chuquicamata is a mine in northern Chile (Figure 35b), some 150 km from the coast at a height of 3 000 m and in one of the driest parts of the Atacama Desert. Chuquicamata means 'land of the Chucos', after an ancient local tribe. The mine is the largest single producer of copper in the world, amounting to 628 000 t or 8.3% of the world's total in 1992 (see Figure 36) and is one of the largest open pits in the world, measuring 3.7 km long by 1.8 km across and over 0.5 km deep (Plate 59). With 500 Mt of ore, grading 1.75% Cu, already removed, reserves still stand at 1.5 billion tonnes, grading 1.1% Cu and 0.12% Mo.

The mineralization is related to a period of mountain building and igneous activity along the Andes during Cretaceous to Early Tertiary times. The granodiorite porphyry at Chuquicamata is highly fractured to form a stockwork of primary copper ore containing 0.5–1.0% Cu, mainly in the form of the sulphides chalcopyrite ($CuFeS_2$), bornite (Cu_5FeS_4) and enargite (Cu_3AsS_4). Zones of enriched secondary mineralization locally grade up to 15% Cu.

(a)

(b)

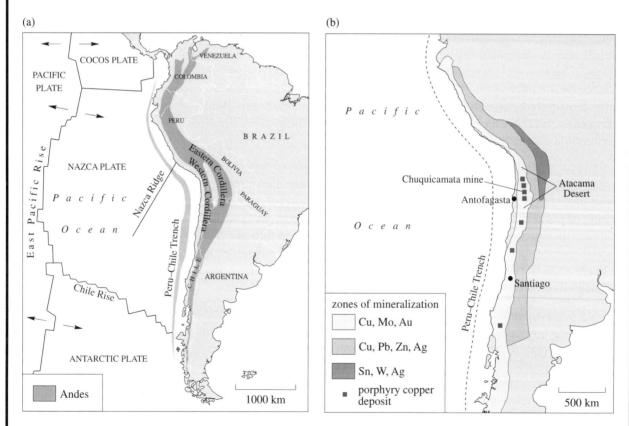

Figure 35 (a) The setting of the Andes in a plate tectonic context; (b) regional zoning of metals in the Andes and the location of Chuquicamata mine in relation to other Chilean porphyry copper deposits.

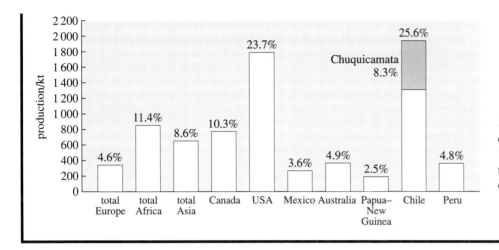

Figure 36 World copper production in 1992, highlighting the contribution of Chuquicamata.

Question 15

Even in regions favourable for porphyry ore formation, mineralized diorites, granodiorites and granites are in the minority. The right combination of conditions is required before a porphyry ore deposit can form. Decide whether the following factors will *favour* or *hinder* the formation of porphyry ore deposits and explain your answers:

(i) a low proportion of water in the initial magma;

(ii) crystallization of magma at deep levels in the crust;

(iii) a high proportion of copper (or molybdenum, or tin) in the magma;

(iv) eruption of magma at the Earth's surface;

(v) crystallization of anhydrous (water-free) minerals from the magma.

Question 16

Chuquicamata is a typical porphyry ore deposit. Hot, aqueous fluid of (i) magmatic and (ii) meteoric origins, as well as (iii) cool percolating meteoric groundwater, have all played roles in concentrating metals within the porphyry copper deposit at Chuquicamata. In terms of the *origin* of the deposit, which of *these* forms of water was arguably the most important and why?

2.5 Summary of Section 2

1 Igneous processes take place in magmatic systems, and involve crystals, immiscible liquids (magma, sulphide melt, oxide melt, water), and gases (as formed when water boils). Chemical and physical processes associated with the separation of crystals or immiscible liquids from magma, give rise to magmatic fractionation, which can produce a range of igneous rock types and may concentrate metals to form ore deposits.

2 Igneous rocks span a range of compositions — from peridotite to gabbro (basalt) to diorite (andesite) to granite (rhyolite) — the formation of which depend on the source of the magma and the extent to which magmatic fractionation has occurred. Different types of ore deposit are associated with particular types of igneous rocks: magmatic segregation deposits are associated with peridotites and gabbros, pegmatite ore deposits with granites, and porphyry ore deposits with diorites, granodiorites and granites.

3   Magmatic segregation deposits separate from hot fluid basaltic magmas when either dense early-formed crystals, or dense immiscible liquids (sulphide or oxide), sink towards the floor of a magma chamber and form cumulate layers. Settling of crystals may produce chromite and magnetite ore deposits; settling of sulphide-rich immiscible liquids may produce ore deposits rich in copper, nickel, gold or platinum; settling of oxide-rich immiscible liquids may produce ore deposits rich in iron or iron–titanium oxides. Development of the multiple layering that is typical of many magmatic segregation deposits requires periodic influxes of hot magma into the magma chamber to reinitiate convection.

4   Pegmatites form from granitic magma after anhydrous minerals have crystallized from it, so enriching the remaining melt in water and sometimes incompatible elements, and thus making it particularly fluid. Pegmatites are not often mineralized, but when they are, they can be enriched in ore minerals of valuable metals, including beryllium, caesium, lithium, niobium, rare earth elements (such as cerium), tantalum, thorium, tin, tungsten, uranium and zirconium, many of which rarely form mineral deposits in other circumstances.

5   Porphyry deposits are formed when metal-rich watery fluids boil and are released explosively from a wet granodioritic magma being emplaced at a high level in the crust. The network of fractures produced, provides pathways for distribution of metal-rich fluids that were derived initially from the magma and subsequently, through convection of meteoric water, from surrounding rocks. The fractures also provide sites for the deposition of ore minerals, as fluids cool and react with wall rocks. Porphyry deposits provide much of the world's copper and molybdenum, as well as substantial quantities of tin, silver and gold as by-products. They are typically low-grade but extremely large deposits.

3 ORE DEPOSITS FORMED BY PROCESSES AT THE EARTH'S SURFACE

The Earth's surface is the part of the Earth with which we are most familiar, even though about 70% of it is covered by water. So, where are the ore deposits? How can we find them? Are they being formed today? If so, and in view of our interest in *renewable* resources, how rapidly are they being formed? In Block 2 we saw that the construction industry uses bulk-mined rocks, often known as 'industrial minerals', such as clays, sands and gravels, many of which were formed as river and glacial deposits in the not-so-distant past — but what of metals and ore deposits? In the UK especially, there may be rather little obvious evidence of ore deposits being formed today, but we shall see that many of the *processes* that have concentrated metals to form ore deposits at the Earth's surface in the past continue to be active in one form or another today.

Before we look at ores formed by surface processes in more detail, let's set mineral deposit formation at the Earth's surface into the context of the conceptual framework provided by the mnemonic, SADE.

The main *Sources* of metals were reviewed in Section 1.5. The most important for ore deposits formed at the Earth's surface is the crust itself, which comprises a wide variety of igneous, sedimentary and metamorphic rocks. In addition, there are the oceans, which can provide a *direct source* from which metals (such as magnesium and lithium) may be extracted, but seawater is more important as an *indirect source* from which dissolved components can be precipitated as evaporites, extracted by organisms and incorporated in sediments.

The main *Agent* that transports and concentrates metals at the Earth's surface is water (as described in Section 1.5.1).

○ What two compositionally distinctive forms of water occur at the Earth's surface?

○ (i) Meteoric water from rainfall: freshwater, which can percolate through soils and permeable rocks to accumulate as groundwater, or become surface run-off to feed rivers and distribute sediments.

(ii) Seawater: saline water, which occupies the oceans and can interact with rocks and sediments, especially along shore lines.

Surface waters are capable of *chemically* transporting metals in solution as ions or as colloidal particles (discussed later) and *physically* transporting ore minerals as grains.

Sites of *Deposition* in this context are at or just beneath the surface of the Earth's crust, both on land and under water. On the surface, sites of deposition are relatively unconstrained; but beneath the surface, deposition is constrained to spaces, such as pores and fractures in rocks. Causes of deposition may be due to changes in the chemical environment, where transport is by solution, or in the physical environment, where mineral grains are concerned.

The forms of *Energy* required to drive the surface processes that concentrate elements are the same as those that drive the water cycle — that is, the *Sun's heat*, which evaporates surface water, and *gravity*, which acts on droplets condensed from water vapour, causing them to fall as rain. The Sun's heat also provides energy to assist chemical reactions (weathering) at the Earth's surface and supports *life*. Living organisms represent an almost insignificant geochemical reservoir for trace metals, but we shall see that, *en masse*, they can contribute significantly to ore-forming processes, especially after death.

Section 3.1 reviews some of the ways in which surface processes can fractionate minerals and elements. It revises the sedimentary and weathering processes discussed in Blocks 1 and 2, and will consolidate your understanding of them as preparation for examining in more detail the processes that are involved in the formation of ore deposits at the Earth's surface.

3.1 Surface processes

The surface part of the rock cycle (outlined in Figure 37) begins with exposure of rocks to physical, chemical and biological forms of weathering, where *weathering* is defined as the *in situ* breakdown of rocks. Weathering not only involves *physical* processes, such as frost shattering, which simply break rock into fragments, but also more complex *chemical* (including biochemical) processes involving rainwater, which break down minerals that are unstable at the Earth's surface, usually by forming more stable minerals and by taking soluble products into solution.

⬤ Which type of weathering is the more likely to *concentrate* metals — physical or chemical?

◯ Chemical weathering, because it involves *selective removal* of chemical constituents in solution during mineral breakdown — a form of sedimentary fractionation — whereas physical weathering only breaks down rock into smaller fragments. Chemical weathering is also important in *liberating* ore mineral grains that subsequently may be transported and concentrated by physical processes.

The removal of exposed rock, which may have been broken down already by weathering, is called *erosion*, and requires an agent of transportation (Figure 37). In water, transportation can take several forms: a *bedload* of solid material, ranging in size from grains to boulders, which rolls and slides along under the influence of a flowing current; a *suspension* of fine-grained material held within a moving body of water; even finer-grained material in *colloidal* form (Block 2, Section 4.1); and a *solution* of dissolved material,

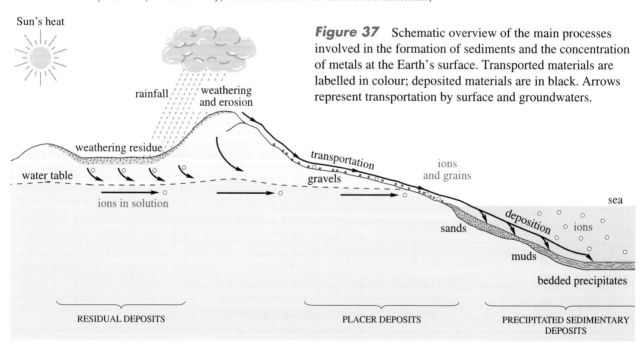

Figure 37 Schematic overview of the main processes involved in the formation of sediments and the concentration of metals at the Earth's surface. Transported materials are labelled in colour; deposited materials are in black. Arrows represent transportation by surface and groundwaters.

dispersed as ions in the water. How deposition occurs depends on the form of material and the mechanism of its transportation, as follows:

1   During *physical* transport, the *energy* of the environment is important, not only in determining what can be eroded, but how easily grains can be moved and subsequently deposited. Light clay particles and sand grains, for example, can be transported more easily, and at lower energies, than pebbles or heavier minerals. Thus, separation of transported grains occurs by *sorting* (Block 2, Section 2.2.1). When the energy of the environment declines, the larger, heavier grains are the first to be deposited, followed by lighter, smaller grains. Such processes are important in forming sedimentary deposits containing ore mineral grains and known as *placer deposits* (Figure 37 and Section 3.4).

2   During *chemical* transport in surface waters, a change in the chemistry of the environment, such as its pH or the oxidizing conditions (as discussed in Section 1.5), can bring about precipitation and deposition both of ions from solution and of *colloidal* particles. For example, neutralization of charges on colloidal clay particles, as occurs when river water mixes with seawater, causes *flocculation* of colloidal clay, leading to deposition. Similar processes may act to deposit other normally insoluble particulates that can also be transported as colloidal particles, such as silica and iron(III) hydroxide. These processes are important in forming precipitated sediments and bedded ore deposits (Figure 37 and Section 3.3).

Properties of natural waters

In order to understand the surface chemical processes that concentrate metals, it is important to appreciate not only that the *solubility* of metal ions changes with the changing properties of a solution, but also how the chemistry of solutions may change in nature. Deep in the Earth, temperature is an important factor affecting the solubility of metals in solution, but in cool surface and groundwaters, pH and oxidizing conditions are more important.

Rainwater contains dissolved carbon dioxide, which makes it mildly acidic (pH ≈ 5.6), and dissolved oxygen, which makes it oxidizing. We noted in Section 1.5 that acidic solutions (containing an excess of H^+ ions over OH^- ions) are capable of reacting with minerals in rocks, especially carbonate minerals in limestones and calcareous sediments:

$$CaCO_3(s) + H^+(aq) = Ca^{2+}(aq) + HCO_3^-(aq) \quad (3.1)$$

limestone   acid   hard water
          solution

The pH values of natural surface waters were given in Figure 18; they generally fall within the range from pH 4 to pH 9. Surface water and groundwater becomes more alkaline as concentrations of the soluble metals sodium, potassium and calcium in solution increase. Alkaline solutions (which contain an excess of OH^- ions over H^+ ions) may react with soluble metal ions to produce insoluble hydroxide (or hydrated oxide) minerals.

The oxidizing nature of rainwater is apparent when minerals are broken down by weathering. Iron is present in many minerals as iron(II), but when released into solution by the action of rainwater it is oxidized to iron(III), to form compounds that are generally insoluble. Iron(III) hydroxide (i.e. hydrated iron(III) oxide) minerals are formed as indicated below:

$$4Fe^{2+}(aq) + 10H_2O(aq) + O_2(aq) =$$
iron(II) ions   oxidizing solution

$$4Fe(OH)_3(s) + 8H^+(aq) \quad (3.2)$$
iron(III) hydroxide

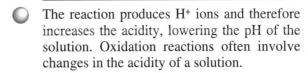 What effect does this oxidation reaction have on the pH of the solution?

The reaction produces H^+ ions and therefore increases the acidity, lowering the pH of the solution. Oxidation reactions often involve changes in the acidity of a solution.

Variations in the oxidation conditions of surface and groundwater solutions occur naturally. Rainwater and free-flowing surface waters are oxidizing; thus, near-surface groundwaters are also oxidizing, but, as they seep through soils and rocks, oxygen is used up by reacting with decaying organic matter (from plants) and with minerals containing metals in a reduced state, so groundwater conditions become more reducing with depth. In carbon- or sulphur-rich conditions, where oxygen is consumed by bacteria, groundwater can become very reducing. This is true of 'surface' environments in which organic material (high in carbon) is decaying, such as swamps and stagnant waters of the sea floor.

Chemical weathering

Chemical weathering at the Earth's surface depends very much on climatic conditions, especially the prevailing temperature and available moisture. We have noted (in the 'Properties of natural waters' box) that rainwater contains dissolved atmospheric gases, which makes it weakly acidic. Bacterial decay of plant matter in soils also produces organic acids, which further acidify rainwater seepage, particularly in warm, humid climates. High temperatures and rainfall therefore promote chemical breakdown of unstable minerals, so chemical weathering is far more important in tropical than in polar or temperate regions.

Some minerals are more susceptible to decomposition by weathering than others. Figure 38 shows the relative stability of the main rock-forming minerals, of which olivine and calcium-rich plagioclase feldspar are the *least stable*, and quartz, the *most stable*. You may recall (from Section 2.1) that this order is roughly the same as the order of crystallization of minerals in igneous rocks (Figure 22). The silicate minerals that crystallize early from magma and are stable at high temperatures are the *least* stable at low temperatures in response to weathering.

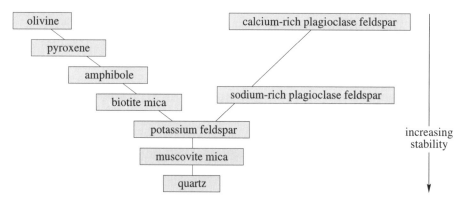

Figure 38 Relative stability of common minerals under weathering conditions.

Question 17

Which rock type is likely to be more susceptible to weathering, peridotite or granite, and why? (*Hint* Refer to Figure 21.)

The chemical weathering of granite and the production of clay deposits (examined in Block 2) can be used to demonstrate how the *removal* of some constituents in *solution* causes the *enrichment* of others in the *residue* left behind. This effect (featured in Figure 37) is a form of concentration process that will be examined in the context of ore deposits in Section 3.2. The action of acidic water on granite under temperate climatic conditions decomposes the feldspars to form the clay mineral, kaolinite, and a solution containing metal ions. Chemically, this reaction is as follows, using potassium feldspar as the example:

$$2KAlSi_3O_8(s) + 2H^+(aq) + H_2O(l) = Al_2Si_2O_5(OH)_4(s) + 2K^+(aq) + 4SiO_2(aq) \quad (3.3)$$

potassium   acid rainwater   kaolinite   ions and silica
 feldspar   in solution

Similar forms of breakdown reaction may be written to describe the weathering of sodium and calcium feldspars, and other unstable rock-forming minerals. The insoluble weathering products of ferromagnesian minerals are usually montmorillonite and iron oxides, whereas micas form illite. Kaolinite, montmorillonite and illite are all types of clay mineral that were introduced in Block 2.

○ What are the products of granite decomposition through chemical weathering in a temperate climate?

○ Granite consists mostly of quartz, feldspars and micas (Figure 21). Chemical weathering breaks down the feldspars and micas to produce insoluble clays, silica (in soluble or colloidal form) and metal ions in solution (the products of reactions such as Equation 3.3). The soluble metals and silica are removed in run-off or in infiltrating water, leaving a residue of weathering-resistant quartz grains and insoluble clay (Figure 39).

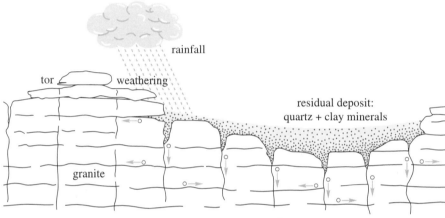

—○ seepage of water containing $Na^+(aq)$, $K^+(aq)$ and $Ca^{2+}(aq)$ ions and silica along joints

Figure 39   Formation of a residual sedimentary deposit of quartz and clay minerals by weathering of granite. Soluble weathering products are removed in infiltrating water.

Although granite is normally a tough rock, suitable for making building blocks and roadstone sets (Plate 24), after prolonged chemical weathering it can be converted to a soft mass of clay and quartz grains, easily worked and sometimes suitable for extracting China clay (as, for example, in Cornwall; although there hydrothermal processes also played a major role in producing kaolinite, see Block 2, Section 4.7). Erosion of these unconsolidated weathering products by surface waters leads eventually to the deposition of the clays as muds, and the quartz grains as sands. Without erosion, the insoluble residues of chemical weathering (here, quartz and clay minerals), would remain in place at the surface to form a **residual deposit** (Figures 37 and 39, and Section 3.2.1). Soluble ions may be removed in infiltrating water or by surface waters, eventually to supply the oceans and, in time, may be precipitated as evaporite deposits or as the skeletons of organisms.

The surface processes of weathering, erosion, transportation and deposition, all have a role in the concentration of metals — sometimes in the form of mineral grains in placer deposits, sometimes as residues in residual deposits, and sometimes as precipitated sedimentary deposits (see Figure 37). They are essentially the same processes as those involved in the formation of sedimentary rocks, such as sandstones, shales and evaporites, but sometimes, metal enrichment may be extreme enough and extensive enough to form an ore deposit.

Question 18

By way of revision of the sedimentary processes that were described in Blocks 1 and 2, match each of the following sedimentary deposits (important 'industrial' minerals):

(i) sand and gravel; (ii) china clay; (iii) evaporites

to whichever of the following processes is most important in its formation:

(a) weathering; (b) physical transport and deposition; (c) chemical transport and deposition.

3.2 Ores formed by chemical leaching and deposition from groundwaters

3.2.1 Residual weathering deposits

In tropical climates, where conditions are warm and humid, chemical weathering of surface rocks is particularly effective (Figure 37). If erosion is minimal, residual products of weathering may form very thick soils, many metres thick, known as **laterites** (from the Latin *later*, meaning 'brick', because of its use as a building material in some tropical countries). Such soils can be formed on most common rock types, but most readily on permeable rocks, accessible to surface water. They consist mainly of kaolinite, and the insoluble hydrated oxides of aluminium (e.g. $Al_2O_3.3H_2O$) and iron(III) (e.g. $Fe_2O_3.H_2O$). It is the iron(III) which gives these soils a deep brick-red colour. Lateritic soils are typically layered as a result of the downward movement of percolating water and the upward movement of moisture in the soil during periodic dry spells. These conditions mobilize soluble ions in solution and transport fine-grained mineral particles through the soil. Deeper layers become richer in clay and upper layers richer in iron. Laterites developed on an iron-rich rock, such as peridotite, may contain as much as 50% iron(III) oxide, but that is rare. Because of their accessibility, some deposits were worked for iron in the past, but mostly their iron content is too low and they are too thin to be of value as iron ores today.

One of the most important types of lateritic ore deposit is developed on weathered peridotite rocks in which nickel is a relatively abundant trace element ($\approx 2\,000$ ppm). It involves the leaching of nickel from the upper layers of the lateritic soil, and deposition, in the form of hydrated nickel silicate minerals, where pH and oxidizing conditions are appropriate for precipitation, namely at the base of the laterite soil and around partially weathered blocks of bedrock (Figure 40). Economic deposits of this kind, grading 1–3% Ni, are known in many tropical areas where there are peridotite rocks at the surface. Such deposits occur in the Pacific Islands of New Caledonia, where mining started as long ago as 1876. It is estimated that laterites account for 60–70% of all economically recoverable nickel (that is, reserves) in land-based deposits, far more than the magmatic nickel sulphide deposits that are mined on a massive scale at Sudbury in Canada and Norilsk in Russia. Cobalt, at grades of only 0.12%, and copper, at 0.3%, are often valuable by-products of nickeliferous laterites. Because of their ease of extraction, grades of only 3.6% Cr can be economic to mine from iron-rich lateritic deposits as a raw material for stainless steel, whereas grades of at least 30% Cr are normally needed for economic mining of magmatic chromite deposits.

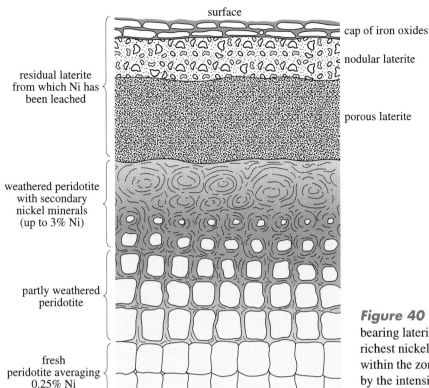

residual laterite
from which Ni has
been leached

weathered peridotite
with secondary
nickel minerals
(up to 3% Ni)

partly weathered
peridotite

fresh
peridotite averaging
0.25% Ni

surface

cap of iron oxides

nodular laterite

porous laterite

Figure 40 Typical section through a nickel-bearing laterite deposit of New Caledonia. The richest nickel deposits lie below the residual laterite within the zone of weathered peridotite, as indicated by the intensity of colour shading.

Why are lateritic deposits economic to mine at relatively low grades?

They occur at the surface largely as poorly consolidated material that can be worked easily in shallow pits. In some deposits, other metals, such as cobalt and copper, may be present as valuable by-products.

Several metals, including nickel, chromium, cobalt, copper, titanium and gold, may be obtained from residual deposits, but by far the most important in quantity is aluminium. Although aluminium is the third most abundant element in the Earth's crust after oxygen and silicon, and the most abundant metal at 8.4%, it is usually combined with other elements in silicate minerals, such as feldspars and micas, from which its extraction would be prohibitively expensive, as it would require vast amounts of energy. So, in what natural form is aluminium most concentrated, and most easily extracted?

In Section 3.1 we saw how chemical weathering can produce the clay mineral kaolinite from feldspars. The aluminium content of kaolinite, expressed in terms of alumina (Al_2O_3), is 40%, which is an enrichment compared with 18–28% Al_2O_3 in feldspars. Thus, both china clay and laterite are relatively rich in aluminium. However, in the warm tropical climates with high rainfall, where laterites form, chemical weathering may progress even further; silica can be leached from kaolinite to form insoluble, hydrated aluminium oxide minerals as follows:

$$Al_2Si_2O_5(OH)_4(s) + H_2O = Al_2O_3.3H_2O(s) + 2SiO_2(aq) \qquad (3.4)$$

kaolinite   insoluble hydrated   soluble
                   aluminium oxides   silica

Laterite rich in hydrated aluminium oxides is called **bauxite**, which takes its name from the village of Les Baux, near Arles in southern France, where the ore was first worked commercially. It occurs as a poorly consolidated, earthy, often nodular deposit, pale red–brown to white in colour. A reddish-brown earthy bauxite is featured in Plate 60.

The ability of percolating surface waters to dissolve silica (SiO$_2$) more readily than alumina (Al$_2$O$_3$) varies over a range of pH values (Figure 41).

⬤ Over what range of pH values shown in Figure 41 would silica be more soluble than alumina?

◯ Between pH 4 and pH 10 the solubility of alumina* is very low, whereas silica is more soluble. Therefore, when silica is released by weathering, it is more easily dissolved than alumina because the pH of most near-surface groundwaters lies within this range (Figure 18).

Notice that very acid waters (pH < 4) can dissolve alumina. This explains why acid rain leaches aluminium from bedrock to produce surface waters that are toxic to both fish and plant life.

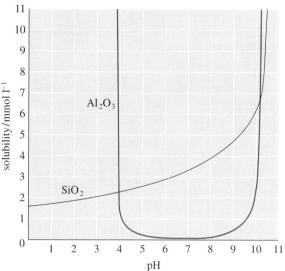

Figure 41 The variation in solubility of Al$_2$O$_3$ and SiO$_2$ in aqueous solution over a range of pH conditions.

If silica is more easily dissolved than alumina by normal surface water solutions, why isn't bauxite more common? Firstly, *extreme* chemical weathering is required in order to break down silicate minerals completely, allowing silica as well as the more soluble metals (Na, K, Ca and Mg) to be removed in solution. But for that to happen, it is also necessary that all the physical requirements for producing thick lateritic soils have been satisfied, such as tropical temperatures and intermittent heavy rainfall, with little erosion by surface run-off. Secondly, quartz is plentiful in many rocks, and isn't that easily dissolved, as it is relatively resistant to solution by weathering (Figure 38). Another problem is that not only aluminium, but also iron and titanium tend to form insoluble oxides in oxidizing environments.

Therefore, even if a laterite deposit is rich enough in alumina for it to be a bauxite, it may also contain significant amounts of insoluble oxides as *impurities*. Only bauxite deposits *low in impurities* can be regarded as ore, because the industrial processing of bauxite for extraction of aluminium sets limits on the composition of ore, demanding at least 50% Al$_2$O$_3$, less than 5% SiO$_2$, a maximum of 20% Fe$_2$O$_3$ and less than 3% TiO$_2$. Consequently, it is necessary for source rocks to have a relatively high aluminium content and a low iron and titanium content, as considered in Table 12.

Question 19

Complete Table 12 to estimate the proportion of alumina in the insoluble residues formed after intense chemical weathering of common igneous rocks. Then decide which of the given igneous rock compositions would be the most suitable to form bauxite ore.

Table 12 Estimation of alumina contents of insoluble weathering products for a range of igneous rock types

	Peridotite	Gabbro	Diorite	Granite
% Al$_2$O$_3$ in rock	4.0	14.1	16.0	14.0
% Fe$_2$O$_3$ + TiO$_2$ in rock	14.1	15.0	9.1	2.9
total % of insoluble oxides (residue)†	18.1			
% Al$_2$O$_3$ content of insoluble residue†	22.1			

† These calculations assume that Al$_2$O$_3$, Fe$_2$O$_3$ and TiO$_2$ are the only insoluble oxides, that decomposition of primary minerals is complete, and all silica and soluble metals (Na, K, Ca and Mg) are lost in solution.

* In acidic solution (pH < 4) aluminium is in the form of the Al^{3+}(aq) ion. In intermediate-pH solutions (pH 4–pH 8), the solubility of the aluminium is low because of the formation of the insoluble hydroxide, Al(OH)$_3$. Above pH 8, aluminium forms the soluble ion [Al(OH)$_4$]$^-$.

Rocks in which the proportion of alumina is very much greater than that of other insoluble constituents are compositionally suitable for the formation of bauxite ores (Table 12); such rocks include granites and other feldspar-rich rocks (preferably low in quartz, which resists weathering). Few bauxite ores can be formed from source rocks with high iron and titanium contents such as gabbros (or basalts) because of their impurity levels. An important factor in bauxite formation is the accessibility of percolating waters for pervasive leaching. Granite may not be an ideal source, unless it is highly fractured or its minerals have been altered previously by hydrothermal fluids, because it is normally rather impermeable. Volcanic ash usually has a more open texture, which gives it higher porosity and permeability, so allowing easy access to surface waters.

Most bauxite deposits, therefore, are found in tropical regions where the climate is hot, with high rainfall, and there are periodic changes from wet to dry conditions, to encourage migration of moisture in the soil. The most important *reserves* are shown in Table 13. They are in equatorial South America, the Caribbean, West Africa, India and Australia. Currently, the largest single bauxite deposit is in Guinea. It contains reserves of at least 180 Mt, at grades of 60% Al_2O_3. This compares with an annual production of about 100 Mt world wide, of which Australia supplies about 40%. Curiously, non-tropical countries such as Hungary and Greece have some of the world's major reserves of bauxite (Table 13). In these countries, bauxites have developed where volcanic ash or wind-borne dust from desert regions came to rest on limestones. Permeable limestones provide an ideal *trap* for residual deposits, since the good drainage they provide minimizes run-off of surface water and hence erosion. The bauxite deposits of Jamaica (see box) are formed in this kind of setting. Because bauxite forms at the Earth's surface, and the deposits are often earthy and poorly consolidated, they are vulnerable to erosion. Therefore, most bauxite deposits are geologically young; only a few are more than 100 Ma old.

Table 13 Major world reserves of bauxite (1993)

Source	Bauxite reserves/Mt	Percentage of total world reserves
Australia	5 620	24.5
Guinea	5 600	24.4
Brazil	2 800	12.2
Jamaica	2 000	8.7
India	1 000	4.4
Guyana	700	3.0
Greece	600	2.6
Surinam	575	2.5
Venezuela	320	1.4
Hungary	300	1.3
others	3 450	15.0
total	22 965	100.0

Just as with other forms of laterite, some bauxite deposits contain metals other than aluminium as by-products. The most valuable of these is probably gold; indeed a bauxite deposit at Boddington, south-east of Perth, contains 1.8 g t^{-1} gold and is one of Australia's largest sites of gold production.

The bauxite deposits of Jamaica

Prior to 1970, the small, sub-tropical island state of Jamaica provided an astonishing 60% of the world's bauxite. The current proportion is about 10% of world production, which still makes Jamaica the world's third largest producer after Australia and Guinea.

Geologically, most of Jamaica is made up of limestones of Tertiary age, which outcrop around a central mountain range (Figure 42a). Aided by high rainfall, which reaches 2 000 mm per year in the mountains, the limestone country is deeply eroded and riddled with caves and underground streams. The numerous bauxite deposits are found as pockets that occupy depressions in the limestone topography (Figure 42b), especially where the limestone is strongly faulted. Rainwater percolates through the fractured rock and readily dissolves the limestone. This produces depressions and provides good drainage, as well as minimizing surface run-off and hence erosion of the bauxite.

A major problem in understanding the formation of these bauxite deposits by chemical weathering of bedrock is the tiny proportion (0.2%) of alumina contained in the limestone. If limestone had been the source, an unrealistically great thickness would have had to have been weathered and dissolved away. It is more likely that the insoluble material came from another source, most probably the weathering of volcanic ash, which fell on the island and collected in the hollows in the limestone.

The bauxite ore is restricted to deposits containing 46–50% Al_2O_3, 3.5–4% SiO_2, 17–22% Fe_2O_3 and 2.4–2.6% TiO_2, although there is considerable variation within a single deposit. Hydrated aluminium oxide ore minerals (for example $Al_2O_3.3H_2O$) are accompanied by lesser amounts of gangue minerals, especially kaolinite, haematite, hydrated iron oxides and resistant accessory minerals.

Jamaica's bauxite production in 1991 was 12 Mt of ore, about a third of which was refined to alumina on the island. Reserves of 2 000 Mt have been quoted — a figure that, in practice, depends more on limitations set for impurities by the refineries than on the cut-off grade for aluminium.

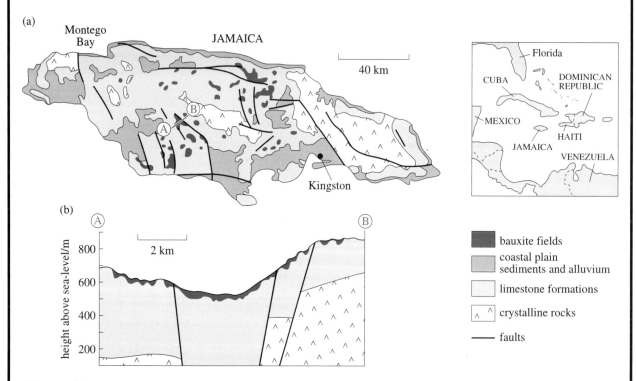

Figure 42 (a) The location of bauxite deposits on the island of Jamaica; (b) a cross-section A–B through a bauxite field in the middle of the island, showing the occurrence of bauxite in pockets.

Question 20

List four of the factors that have contributed towards the formation of bauxite deposits in Jamaica.

3.2.2 Secondary enrichment deposits

So far, we have considered mainly the *residual* products of weathering pro-cesses — those left behind after water has removed soluble components from surface rocks. Here we consider the fate of the metal ions that are *dissolved* and carried in solution with percolating groundwaters (Figures 37 and 39).

When it first enters soils and rocks, percolating rainwater is oxidizing and slightly acidic (see box 'Properties of natural waters'). As this solution interacts with organic matter in the soil, and metal ions in reduced states, oxygen is used up and levels decrease, so groundwater becomes more reducing with depth. Whether the conditions are oxidizing or reducing, and by how much, determines the oxidation state of the metals present and how soluble their compounds are. In particular, iron(II) compounds tend to be quite soluble, whereas iron(III) compounds tend to be insoluble. Not all metals are more insoluble in higher oxidation states, however, as we shall see shortly.

Let's look at the way metals may be mobilized when a *mineral deposit* is affected by percolating groundwater. Under near-surface conditions, many sulphide minerals break down by reaction with percolating rainwater in the oxidizing environment. For example, when chalcopyrite is oxidized, it breaks down to form the insoluble iron(III) hydroxide (i.e. hydrated iron(III) oxide) and soluble copper and sulphate ions, as follows:

$$4CuFeS_2(s) + \underbrace{10H_2O(l) + 17O_2(aq)}_{} = 4Fe(OH)_3(s) + \underbrace{4Cu^{2+}(aq) + 8SO_4^{2-}(aq) + 8H^+(aq)}_{} \quad (3.5)$$

$$\text{chalcopyrite} \qquad \text{rainwater} \qquad\qquad \text{iron(III)} \qquad\qquad \text{soluble ions}$$
$$\text{hydroxide}$$

At the weathered surface of the deposit, as indicated in Figure 43, the insol-uble iron(III) hydroxide produced in this reaction forms a *residual deposit* (analogous to laterite formation), composed largely of limonite ($Fe_2O_3.H_2O$), as a surface layer, reddish-brown to bright orange in colour (rather like rust), and

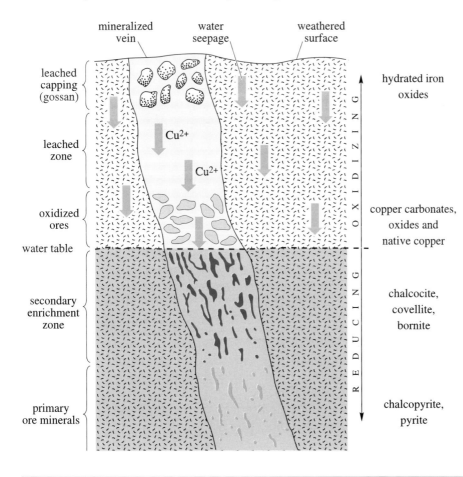

Figure 43 Generalized section through a sulphide (chalcopyrite)-bearing mineral deposit, where leaching of soluble (copper) ions in oxid-izing groundwater occurs above the water table and secondary enrichment of (copper) sulphide minerals in reducing ground-water occurs beneath the water table.

called iron cap or **gossan**. The colourful appearance of gossan at the surface is distinctive, and has revealed many sulphide mineral deposits to prospectors. In the oxidized zone of weathering the decomposition of sulphides, such as that of chalcopyrite above (Equation 3.5), is in part, at least, a biochemical reaction. The bacterium *Thiobacillus ferrooxidans* helps to oxidize iron sulphides and is now used in modern ore processing schemes to leach metals from their ore.

What, then, happens to the *soluble ions* that are released and pass downwards with the percolating groundwater? Some may combine with bicarbonate (HCO_3^-) ions from rainwater, to form carbonate minerals in the *oxidizing* conditions that prevail above the water table (Figure 43). Copper in solution then precipitates as the colourful carbonate minerals, green malachite ($CuCO_3.Cu(OH)_2$) and blue azurite ($2CuCO_3.Cu(OH)_2$). Copper may also be deposited as the native metal (Plate 61) close to the water table. However, much copper remains in solution until it reaches the water table, beneath which groundwater conditions are *reducing* (Figure 43). Sulphide minerals in the deposit do not break down under the reducing conditions, but the influx of metal ions from above brings about chemical reactions with the **primary ore minerals** to form new **secondary ore minerals**. In a copper-rich sulphide deposit, secondary minerals include covellite (CuS), chalcocite (Cu_2S) and bornite (Cu_5FeS_4); for example

$$CuFeS_2 + Cu^{2+}(aq) = 2CuS(s) + Fe^{2+}(aq) \qquad (3.6)$$
$$\text{chalcopyrite} \qquad\qquad\qquad \text{covellite}$$

In effect, copper ions replace iron in the iron-bearing primary sulphides, and iron is removed as Fe^{2+} ions in solution under the reducing conditions below the water table. The result is that the secondary copper minerals so produced are even richer in copper than the primary minerals.

Do any other metals behave like copper in similar circumstances? We can work out which might by examining Table 14, which gives comparative solubilities under oxidizing and reducing groundwater conditions for several metal ions.

Table 14 Solubilities* of selected metals under oxidizing (sulphate-bearing) and reducing (sulphide-bearing) groundwater conditions

Metal	Oxidizing conditions solubility/mol l^{-1}	Reducing conditions solubility/mol l^{-1}
Hg	10^{-14}	10^{-32}
Pb	10^{-6}	10^{-7}
Ag	1	10^{-15}
Cu	1	10^{-14}
Zn	1	10^{-4}

* Solubility values in mol l^{-1} represent the relative proportions of metal ions that could exist in a saturated aqueous solution.

○ Which of the metals in Table 14 are much more soluble under the oxidizing conditions?

○ Silver, copper and zinc have the highest solubility values.

So, silver, copper and zinc might be expected to enter solution and be *leached* from minerals where groundwater conditions are sulphate-bearing and oxidizing. Mercury and lead are so insoluble that they are unlikely to be leached under these conditions (Table 14).

○ Which of the three metals that are much more soluble under the oxidizing conditions are more insoluble under the reducing conditions?

○ Of the leachable metals, silver and copper are more insoluble than zinc in sulphide-bearing reducing solutions.

So, under reducing conditions below the water table, silver and copper sulphide minerals are more likely to be precipitated. The overall effect is that metals very soluble in oxidizing solutions and insoluble under reducing conditions are leached from near the surface and then precipitated below the water table to form **secondary enrichment deposits** (Figure 43). This process has important implications for the form and distribution of near-surface mineralization, particularly for dispersed ore deposits.

○ For which type of dispersed ore deposit have we already hinted at the importance of secondary enrichment?

○ Porphyry copper deposits.

At the Chuquicamata mine (Section 2.4), for example, secondary enrichment locally reaches grades of 15% Cu. Secondary enrichment is also important for silver, which has solubility properties similar to those of copper (Table 14). In silver deposits, secondary enrichment grades have been known to reach 25% Ag locally, though 0.2–0.3% is more normal.

An example of the scale and setting of secondary enrichment is provided by the Inspiration porphyry copper deposit at Miami, Arizona, featured in Figure 44. Above the water table the rocks are leached, whereas below it they are enriched in copper sulphides. The leached capping is very low in copper, has no economic value, and must be removed as overburden in order to mine the underlying copper ores; but at least it doesn't need to be processed. As the copper is concentrated in the enriched zone, it means that a smaller volume of ore has to be processed for the same yield than if there had been no secondary enrichment.

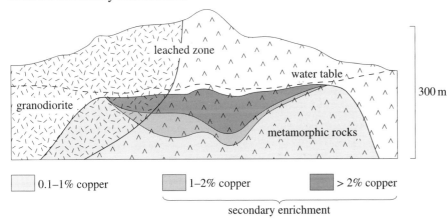

Figure 44 A cross-section through the Inspiration ore body at Miami, Arizona, showing the relationship between the leached zone, the zone of secondary enrichment (with high-grade copper ore) and the water table. Levels of (0.1–1%) copper are more normal for a porphyry copper deposit.

3.3 Ores formed through chemical transport and deposition by surface waters

Surface waters include run-off into rivers, and accumulations in lakes and the oceans. Although seawater contains a far larger concentration of dissolved metal ions than freshwater, an important source of its metals is from rivers through weathering of continental crust. Proof that land-derived waters carry significant quantities of *dissolved* salts is evident where rivers flow into land-locked lakes, which only lose water through evaporation, and produce salt flats, or salt lakes, such as the Dead Sea.

○ What processes other than evaporation were mentioned earlier which might cause precipitation of metal ions as salts?

○ The main causes of changes in solubility mentioned were changing temperature, pH or the oxidizing condition of the solution (Sections 1.5 and 3.1).

Another form of transport is as minute *colloidal particles* (Block 2, Section 4.1). Substances in colloidal form are essentially insoluble, but fail to precipitate because the individual submicroscopic particles carry the same type of electrostatic charge (+ or −). As like charges repel, aggregation of the particles to a size at which they are large enough to precipitate is inhibited. Colloidal transport is most effective in solutions with a low concentration of metal ions, such as freshwater. If the concentration of ions in the solution (that is, its salinity) increases, the charges on the colloidal particles are neutralized and the tiny particles are then able to coalesce to form larger particles — that is, to *flocculate* — and settle out as a chemically formed sediment. Substances often regarded as insoluble can be transported very effectively as colloids. They include silica, clay minerals, sulphides and iron(III) hydroxide.

○ In what geographic setting might you expect the salinity of surface waters to change markedly, so bringing about flocculation and deposition of colloidal material?

○ At river mouths, where freshwater (with low salinity) enters the sea (with high salinity).

The flocculation process commonly involves *adsorption*, the loose attachment of metal ions from the saline water on to the surface of colloidal particles. Although Na^+ and K^+ ions are the most readily available, they tend to remain in solution. Clay particles may collect trace metal ions such as Cu^{2+}, Pb^{2+} and Zn^{2+} from the seawater. These ions are more effective in bringing about flocculation of colloids because of their higher charge.

However, a more important mechanism by which metals are concentrated from seawater, especially copper and zinc, is by adsorption on to *organic* material. Accumulation of this organic material forms carbonaceous black shales in ocean bottom environments where conditions become very reducing on account of decaying organic matter. The resulting shales are often rich in trace metals, such as copper, zinc, molybdenum and uranium. Though they are not rich enough to constitute ore deposits, such metal-rich or **metalliferous** shales have the potential to be *scavenged* by hydrothermal solutions after burial, and may be important as a *source* of metals, as we shall see in Section 4.

Although near-surface processes are most familiar and visible to us, in practice the chemistry of deposition in surface environments is poorly understood. This is at least in part because chemical reactions are much slower at the low temperatures of the Earth's surface than those occurring at depth (at higher temperatures) and are more difficult to investigate experimentally in a laboratory. Also, the chemical behaviour of ionic and particulate material in surface waters is affected in subtle ways by many factors including acidity, oxidizing conditions and biochemical activity. Therefore, the following discussion of precipitated sedimentary deposits is limited in the first part to the ores of iron, by far the most widely used of all metals, and in the second part to manganese nodules, deposits that are not really ores at all, at least not yet, but have great potential.

3.3.1 Bedded iron ores

Iron is by far the most important metal of the modern world, amounting to almost 90% of all primary (mined) metal production. Perhaps this is not surprising, because iron is the second most abundant metal in the Earth's crust (5.8%). What is more surprising is that today's average minimum exploitable grade of 50% iron is so high. This is because iron can be extracted most easily by smelting its oxides, haematite (Fe_2O_3) and magnetite (Fe_3O_4). Both of these minerals are stable at the Earth's surface, contain a high proportion of iron, and form highly concentrated deposits. Years ago, as you saw in Video Band 1: *The Great Iron and Steel Rollercoaster*, grades of 25% iron were economic to mine, and before that, ores rich in the carbonate mineral, siderite ($FeCO_3$) were obtained from coal mines. Iron is not easily extracted from the silicate minerals of igneous rocks, and, although the iron sulphides are probably the most common sulphide minerals, they are not as rich in iron as the oxide minerals, nor is it as easy to extract iron, at least not without creating pollution from sulphurous gases.

Concentrations of iron oxides and carbonates, forming **bedded iron ore deposits** in ancient sedimentary rock sequences, are thought to have been formed mainly through chemical precipitation from solution. But how can iron be transported in solution? With *oxidizing conditions* prevailing at the Earth's surface today, it is common for iron to form hydrated iron(III) oxides, which are very insoluble and readily precipitate, encrusting available surfaces or accumulating as sludge. Iron is much more soluble in its reduced, iron(II), state, but is likely to occur in solution in this form only in environments such as swamps, where rotting vegetation creates acidic, reducing conditions.

⬤ How, then, might iron(II), transported in reducing waters, be precipitated?

◯ Precipitation may occur where iron(II)-bearing swamp waters overflow into active and thus aerated, and oxygenated, drainage channels. Iron(II) is oxidized and insoluble hydrated iron(III) oxide is formed. It may precipitate and settle directly, or may be transported in colloidal form before eventual precipitation and deposition. In water with a high bicarbonate (HCO_3^-) ion concentration, siderite ($FeCO_3$) may form.

Commonly, the iron ores used early in the Industrial Revolution of western Europe were carbonates occurring as 'black band' iron ores in Carboniferous Coal Measure sequences, which were mined along with coal. Coal-forming swamps in Carboniferous times provided ideal conditions for the solution of iron(II); precipitation of siderite then occurred when swamp waters mixed with water carrying a significant concentration of bicarbonate ions.

As described in Video Band 1, the natural coexistence of coal and iron ore was an important factor in the development of the iron smelting industry during the Industrial Revolution. The main problem with 'black band' iron ores was their small volume, so supplies were unable to match the growing demand. In Europe, the heart of the Industrial Revolution, a new source had to be found. This was provided in Britain by ironstones, mainly of Jurassic age, along a belt from Oxfordshire through Lincolnshire to Cleveland (see *The Geological Map* booklet, p. 29), and in central Europe by ironstones of the Alsace–Lorraine and Salzgitter areas. These ores, which occur as bedded units 10–15 m thick and extend for tens of kilometres, were worked extensively in Britain until the 1970s.

The Jurassic ironstones largely consist of a hydrous iron silicate mineral called berthierine, which forms ooliths (that is, sand-sized grains with a concentric layered structure) and siderite, which forms the matrix between the ooliths (Figure 45a). The origin of these ooliths is uncertain, though it is believed that they were formed by precipitation of iron minerals in a shallow marine environment. In these circumstances, oxidizing conditions usually prevail, but berthierine and siderite both contain iron(II), so how could soluble Fe^{2+} ions have been transported to the site of deposition without oxidation and precipitation as iron(III) compounds? It is not by chance that the Jurassic ironstones of Europe formed offshore of coal swamps similar to those of the Carboniferous. Fe^{2+} ions in solution in swamp waters could have been *adsorbed* on to fine-grained organic colloidal matter, and carried in this way, so avoiding precipitation as iron(III) hydroxide in free-flowing oxygenated river water. In the open sea, these colloids, possibly accompanied by colloidal silica, were precipitated to form iron-rich muds, from which the ooliths were formed.

As ores, the Jurassic ironstones cause problems in the smelting process because they contain high amounts of calcium, silica and phosphorus. The open pits of eastern England are no longer worked because richer, more easily smelted ores became available. Such deposits were found initially near Lake Superior in North America, but ores of the same type are now worked in many other parts of the world, including Russia, Ukraine, Australia, China and Brazil. Some of these deposits extend for hundreds of kilometres and may be as much as 500 m thick. They formed as sediments some 1 900 to 2 750 Ma ago, in Precambrian times. As shown in Figure 45b and Plate 62, they comprise finely banded layers, several millimetres thick, rich in the iron oxide minerals haematite and magnetite, and alternating with layers of chert (rock composed of precipitated silica). For this reason they are known as **banded iron formation** (BIF) deposits. Sedimentary structures suggest that deposition occurred in a low-energy environment; ripple marks and sun cracks indicate that they formed in shallow water. The absence of sediment grains derived from pre-existing rock suggests that deposition may have been far from land or, more likely, near a low land surface with little erosion. So, how might the iron have been transported to form BIF?

○ Did swamps with decaying plant material, like those of the Jurassic and Carboniferous, which provided organic colloids and reducing conditions, exist in Precambrian times?

○ No, because plants only colonized land areas about 400 Ma ago.

So we cannot invoke transportation mechanisms that applied in Jurassic or Carboniferous times in the Precambrian. However, the Earth's atmosphere during early Precambrian times was very different from today. Although free oxygen was becoming more abundant between 2 500 and 2 000 Ma ago, it was still at a relatively low level, and the relatively high level of CO_2 in the atmosphere may have allowed iron to be transported as $Fe^{2+}(aq)$ ions. However, algae did exist and they may have assisted in the precipitation of iron as iron(III) oxides. The restriction of BIF deposits to a particular period of the Earth's history suggests that a rather special combination of atmospheric and oceanic conditions — possibly even biological circumstances — was responsible for BIF deposition.

(a)

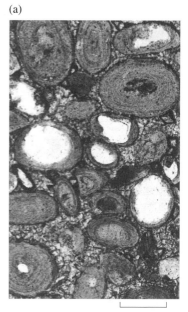

1 mm

(b)

1 cm

Figure 45 Sedimentary iron ores: (a) Northamptonshire Ironstone, containing ooliths of berthierine set in a matrix of siderite; (b) alternating bands (2–8 mm wide) of chert and iron oxide in a sample of banded iron formation.

The amount of iron occurring in BIF world wide has been estimated at 10^{14} tonnes, but only a small proportion of this is currently economic. BIF in which oxide minerals predominate average 30–35% iron, but there are also silicate- and carbonate-bearing BIF, which contain only 25–30% iron. Economic deposits, enriched to levels in excess of 60% iron, have formed where silica has been leached from the layers of chert, and haematite and magnetite have recrystallized, a process more reminiscent perhaps of residual and secondary enrichment deposit formation (see also box 'Iron ores of the Hamersley Range, Western Australia'). World resources of iron ore are estimated to exceed 800 billion (8×10^{11}) tonnes, and contain more than 230 billion (2.3×10^{11}) tonnes of iron. This amount is many times in excess of the annual production of iron ore, currently less than 10^9 tonnes, and therefore iron reserves would seem to have a relatively unrestricted lifetime of at least 230 years.

Iron ores of the Hamersley Range, Western Australia

Reserves of iron ore in the Hamersley region of Western Australia (Figure 46) amount to 40×10^9 t at grades exceeding 55% Fe. This is all the more remarkable, because for many years they had been overlooked. Indeed, in Australia in the late nineteenth century, iron ore was seen as being of 'no great value', and before the Second World War an embargo was put on Australian exports of iron ore by the Commonwealth Government because it was thought that reserves were running out and the country should conserve its stocks! In addition, the state government prevented prospectors from retaining rights to any discovery, and thereby removing incentives for exploration. It wasn't until the early 1960s that these regulations were lifted. Intensive exploration followed, which established much of the known reserve during the following ten years.

Many surface rocks in the Hamersley Range weather to an orangish or reddish brown (Plate 63), revealing large areas composed of Precambrian banded iron formations between 2 750 and 2 300 Ma old. The highest-grade ores form units 2–15 m thick, separated by shales, chert and iron carbonate-bearing sediments. The most productive ore deposits have undergone secondary enrichment and consist largely of magnetite with variable amounts of haematite. The ore mined today grades more than 60% iron, with impurities less than 4% SiO_2, less than 2% Al_2O_3 and less than 0.1% P_2O_5. Secondary enrichment appears to be related to the present erosion surface, but the same surface was exposed in Tertiary times (many tens of millions of years ago). Even more remarkably, fragments of *enriched* ores are present in conglomerates 1 800 Ma old, which indicates a much earlier origin.

In the early 1990s, Australia was the world's third largest iron ore producer behind Ukraine and Brazil. It was then producing about 120 Mt of ore per year, most of it from the Hamersley region. One of the largest deposits is at Mt Tom Price, an ore body 8 km by 1.2 km, containing 500 Mt of ore grading 64% iron. The workings at Mt Tom Price are shown in Plate 64.

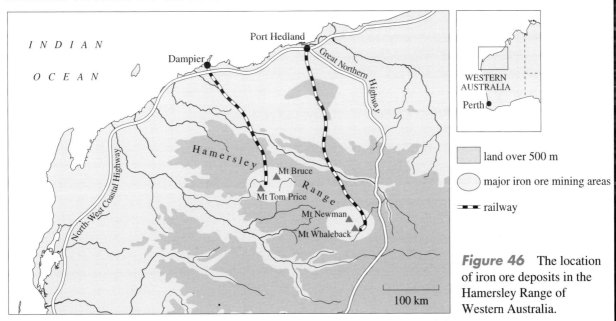

Figure 46 The location of iron ore deposits in the Hamersley Range of Western Australia.

Question 21

(a) Much of the importance of iron to the industrialized world is due to its versatility in use, particularly in steels. Even more important is its low price, which is a reflection of its availability. Give three reasons why iron ore is readily available in large quantities.

(b) Suggest why the substitution of iron and steel products might be beneficial for resource conservation even if the cost of iron ore is relatively low and there are abundant supplies for the foreseeable future.

3.3.2 Manganese nodules

Currently more of a curiosity than a resource, **manganese nodules** are objects with the appearance of 'burnt baked potatoes'. They often occur in abundance scattered over the surface of deep ocean floors (Figure 47a), where the rate of particulate sedimentation is slow. The nodules are composed of hydrated iron and manganese oxides, built up in layers around some form of nucleus, to form a banded (often concentrically) internal structure (Figure 47b). Deposits of similar composition also occur as encrustations on rock surfaces of the ocean floor, but the attraction of manganese nodules as a resource is that they rest on the surface, are loose, and could be picked up easily. However, a disadvantage for exploitation is that, although they may cover huge areas, they occur as a very thin layer.

(a)

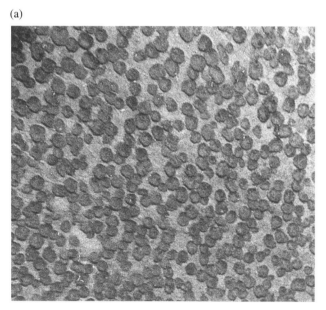

(b)

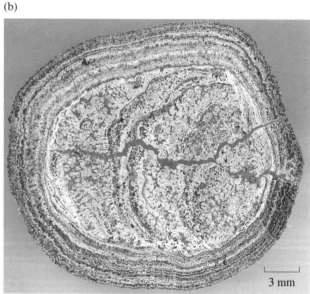

3 mm

Figure 47 (a) A view of manganese nodules lying on the ocean floor.

(b) A cross-section through a manganese nodule, showing concentric layering.

Table 15 gives an average composition for manganese nodules. Although manganese is just about the most abundant metal in the nodules, and is enriched over a hundred times compared with its average abundance in continental crust (Table 15), the deposits from which manganese ores are obtained today are not these nodules, but sedimentary deposits similar to BIF. They contain even greater enrichments of manganese than nodules, and are much more accessible: the average minimum exploitable grade is 35% Mn. Manganese nodules are therefore unlikely to become manganese ores in the near future. Their real importance is due to their content of other metals.

Table 15   Average abundance of elements in manganese nodules compared with average crustal abundances

Element	Average abundance in manganese nodule/ppm	Average abundance in continental crust/ppm	Concentration factor
manganese	160 000	1 400	114.3
iron	155 000	70 700	2.2
silicon	86 000	267 700	0.3
aluminium	28 000	84 100	0.3
calcium	25 000	52 900	0.5
sodium	19 000	23 000	0.8
magnesium	18 000	32 000	
potassium	6 500	9 100	
titanium	6 500	5 400	1.2
nickel	4 800	105	
cobalt	2 800	29	
copper	2 600	75	
barium	2 000	250	8.0
lead	900	8	112.5
strontium	820	260	3.2
zinc	780	80	
zirconium	650	100	6.5
chromium	35	185	0.2

Question 22

Use the average compositions of manganese nodules and average crustal abundances given in Table 15 to calculate the six concentration factors left blank, and decide which metals are enriched by more than a factor of 10 in manganese nodules.

In total, the concentration of the trace metals in manganese nodules amounts to more than 1%. In relation to cut-off grades of land-based low-grade dispersed deposits, such abundances would make exploitation attractive.

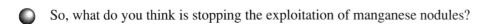 So, what do you think is stopping the exploitation of manganese nodules?

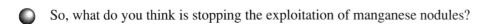 Most obviously, the oceanic environment and the depth from which they must be dredged (in excess of 3 km) poses technical difficulties for collection, and greatly increases costs, although prototype mining equipment has been developed.

Currently, a combined nickel, cobalt, copper, lead and zinc grade of over 3% would be needed for dredging to be an economic proposition. Such compositions occur only in the north-east tropical Pacific between California and Hawaii, where the yield of nodules could be as much as 15 billion tonnes.

Another problem is ownership: most nodules occur in international waters outside 200 mile limits, the Exclusive Economic Zones within which coastal states have rights to sea-bed resources. So no one owns them, and mining can only go ahead with international agreement. Despite a number of international conferences during the 1980s, no agreement was reached on how sea-bed mining should be managed and how profits should be distributed. A large number of Third World countries supported exploitation, seeing opportunities to share in profits, but existing mineral producers and developed countries were opposed to it. In the late 1980s and early 1990s, depressed mineral prices and discoveries of new deposits elsewhere have 'undermined' hopes of profitable exploitation, so interest has waned.

There are also environmental considerations. To mine economically what is a rather thin and discontinuous layer of nodules, would need a very large area to be dredged, so disturbing sediments and organisms living on or within the ocean floor. Such large-scale disturbance of the ocean-floor environment would be undesirable and likely to encounter strong opposition.

Manganese nodules are therefore an example of a *conditional resource*, which is uneconomic to exploit at present but ready to spring onto the world scene if the cost of recovery was reduced, or if the value of the metals increased. If they were to become a viable source of metals, the availability of such vast reserves could have serious repercussions on the economics and viability of conventional mining. It has been quoted that the potential copper resource from manganese nodules is 0.7×10^9 t, compared to the total land-based resource of 1.6×10^9 t of copper.

How do manganese nodules form? As for many other sedimentary deposits, the process of precipitation is likely to be a complex one. *Clues* may be found nearer to home. In upland Britain, in streams and lakes fed by waters from peaty moorland or boggy hillsides, we find rocks and pebbles coated with a very dark brown, almost black, layer. This layer consists of hydrated iron(III) and manganese(IV) oxides. In the acidic and reducing waters draining boggy areas, iron and manganese are dissolved as *soluble* iron(II) and manganese(II) ions. When these waters enter a more agitated (hence aerated) and oxidizing environment of a lake or stream, oxidation of these ions leads to the precipitation of *insoluble* hydrated oxides of iron(III) and manganese(IV). This similarity in behaviour of iron and manganese may explain their high concentrations (Table 15) in manganese nodules on the deep ocean floor. Although the formation of manganese nodules is not fully understood, subtle changes in chemistry, especially the oxidizing conditions, of ocean bottom waters may bring about intermittent precipitation of iron, manganese and other metals to form layers on solid surfaces and around seed nuclei on the ocean floor.

Figure 48 shows the distribution of manganese nodules in the world's oceans. Why should the abundance of nodules be so low near to the continents and along the Equator? The reason is that sediment is deposited so rapidly in both these areas that it hinders the growth of nodules. Near to the continents, it is land-derived sediments that are the problem; in equatorial regions, it is the high productivity of plankton that supplies a steady rain of organic sediment.

It is a curious fact that although manganese nodules occur where sedimentation rates are slow, their growth is 1 000 times slower than the accumulation of surrounding sediment. Dating growth layers tells us that it takes 20–40 Ma for a 10 cm nodule to grow! So nodules can hardly be considered as renewable resources, although they are forming over vast areas of the ocean floor today. How is it, then, that they are not submerged by sediment?

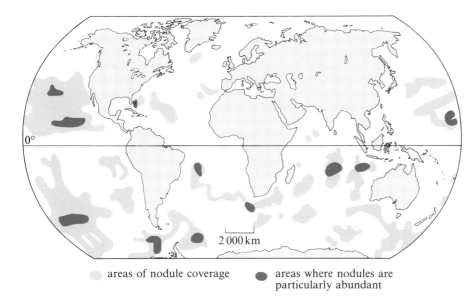

Figure 48 The distribution of manganese nodules in the world's oceans.

● areas of nodule coverage   ● areas where nodules are particularly abundant

One idea is that they could be moved by currents and roll over the surrounding sediment, as the surface builds up. However, nodules are not entirely regular in shape; their under surfaces tend to be uneven, suggesting that they remain the same way up for long periods. Another possibility might be that organisms disturb underlying sediment and keep the nodules at the surface. To date there is no really satisfactory explanation.

Question 23

Explain why manganese nodules are not currently included in the world's metal reserves.

3.4 Ores formed through physical transport and deposition by surface waters: placer deposits

In Blocks 1 (Section 3.5.2) and 2 (Sections 2.2.2 and 4.2) you saw how transport of rock and mineral particles by wind, ice, and, more especially, water can *sort* sediment into material of different grain sizes.

○ What property of the transporting medium most influences the degree of *sorting*?

○ The *energy of the transporting* environment is the important controlling factor.

Strictly, the energy of the transporting environment itself determines what grains can be transported; so it is a *change* in the energy of the environment that sorts grains. For example, a high-energy environment such as a fast-flowing stream may be able to transport a range of grain sizes from the finest-grained clay minerals to pebbles and rock fragments. A slackening of the current, and hence a *decrease* in the energy of the environment, causes larger and heavier grains to be deposited, whereas the smaller, lighter particles remain in suspension or move as bedload. Clay minerals are deposited at a later stage when the energy of the environment is very low: especially in lakes, lagoons, estuaries and the deeper parts of the oceans. An *increase* in the energy of the environment, especially if it is turbulent, can be equally effective in sorting. If sediment containing quartz and clay minerals is stirred up, for example by waves on beaches or by rapids in rivers, the lighter clay minerals can be removed, to be deposited elsewhere, and the larger quartz grains will be left behind; this process is known as **winnowing**. Whichever way the change of energy occurs, provided sorting is efficient, a mixture of quartz and clay minerals can be separated into deposits of quartz-rich sand and clay-rich mud.

Sorting by selective deposition from flowing water is not only a mechanism for concentrating sediment grains of a particular size, but also of a particular density. This means that ore minerals, many of which are much denser than rock-forming silicate minerals, can also be concentrated because they are the first to be deposited. They are frequently trapped in locations where flow rates rapidly diminish, or are left behind by winnowing. Accumulations of ore minerals produced in this way are known as **placer deposits**.

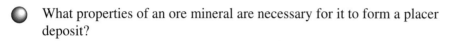 What properties of an ore mineral are necessary for it to form a placer deposit?

High density, to assist sorting, and durability against both chemical attack and physical disintegration.

Minerals prone to chemical alteration, such as iron sulphides that are easily oxidized, are unlikely to survive weathering or transportation and subsequent deposition as detrital grains. **Detrital grains** are derived from pre-existing rocks; they are resistant minerals or fragments of rock that have survived weathering and transport. Soft, or easily fractured minerals, especially those that are well cleaved, become severely worn or broken down during transport, and the very fine grains that result are not easily separated and concentrated by sorting processes. So, hard, poorly cleaved minerals, which are stable during weathering, will be most durable and likely to persist as sand-sized detrital grains and form placer deposits on sorting and deposition. Indeed, placer minerals must be *chemically stable* in order to be liberated by chemical breakdown of their host rock and *physically stable* to be transported and concentrated by physical sorting processes.

Table 16 Density and hardness of some ore minerals

Mineral	Formula	Density*/t m^{-3}	Hardness†	Cleavage
ilmenite	FeTiO$_3$	4.7	5.5	none
bornite	Cu$_5$FeS$_4$	5.1	3	poor
molybdenite	MoS$_2$	4.9	1.5	good
cassiterite	SnO$_2$	7.0	6.5	poor
columbite	FeNb$_2$O$_6$	5.5	6	weak
barite	BaSO$_4$	4.5	3	good
zircon	ZrSiO$_4$	4.7	7.5	none
gold	Au	19.0	2	none

* Densities of common rock-forming minerals range from about 2.5 to about 3.0 t m^{-3}.

† As measured by Moh's scale, ranging from 1 (softest) to 10 (hardest). Gypsum is 2, and diamond 10 on this scale. Minerals with hardness values greater than about 5 are considered hard. Apatite, the main mineral in teeth, has a hardness of 5.

Question 24

Table 16 lists eight minerals with their density, hardness and cleavage. Which *five* would you expect to find in placer deposits and why?

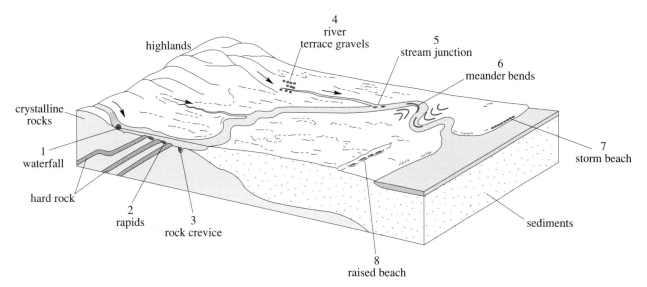

Figure 49 illustrates sites where placer deposits may be found. Sites 1–4 are sediment traps in rivers, where heavier mineral grains can be trapped and rapidly flowing river waters carry away the lighter silicate minerals. Sites 5 and 6 are locations where the current slackens, allowing selective deposition of heavier mineral grains. At site 5, a fast-flowing stream meets a more sluggish stream, and at site 6 the current slows on the inside of a river meander. Sites 1–6 are all *alluvial* deposits; sites 7 and 8 are *coastal* deposits. Site 7 is a storm beach, where heavy mineral grains are retained by winnowing due to wave action. In areas where sea-level has fallen relative to the land surface, old, abandoned beaches may occur inland. These are known as raised beaches (site 8) and may also contain beach placer deposits.

Figure 49 Typical locations of placer deposits in alluvial and coastal environments. Erosion of the highlands is the ultimate source of heavy mineral grains. Numbered sites are referenced in the text.

Table 17 lists the most important minerals to be mined from placer deposits. Dense oxide minerals and native metals, often termed **heavy minerals**, predominate. The most abundant placer minerals are magnetite, ilmenite and rutile, which are the main heavy mineral constituents of 'black sands', as beach placer deposits are often called. Of course, any one placer deposit will not contain all of these minerals: its mineral content will depend on the *source rocks* from which the sediment was derived and the *efficiency of sorting* in the depositional environment. Notice that Table 17 reveals how the efficiency of sorting is greater in beach environments; these deposits tend to contain the more abundant, *lower density* placer minerals. The *higher density* placer minerals are generally more important in alluvial environments.

Table 17 Ore minerals commonly recovered from placer deposits

Metal	Ore mineral	Density/$t\,m^{-3}$	Main environment
titanium	rutile, TiO_2	4.2	beach sand
zirconium	zircon, $ZrSiO_4$	4.6–4.7	beach sand
titanium	ilmenite, $FeTiO_3$	4.7	beach sand
rare earth elements	monazite, $CePO_4$	4.8–5.5	beach sand
iron	magnetite, Fe_3O_4	5.2	beach sand
niobium	columbite, $FeNb_2O_6$	5.2–7.9	alluvial
tin	cassiterite, SnO_2	6.8–7.1	alluvial
tantalum	tantalite, $FeTa_2O_6$	7.9–8.2	alluvial
gold	native metal, Au	15.0–19.3	alluvial
platinum	native metal, Pt	14.0–19.0	alluvial

Many important placer minerals form originally by crystallization as accessory minerals in igneous rocks.

⬤ Which type of igneous rock is likely to be the best source of placer deposits containing (i) cassiterite, (ii) zircon, and (iii) magnetite. (*Hint* Refer back to Section 2.1.1.)

◯ These minerals occur as accessory minerals in igneous rocks as follows: (i) cassiterite in granites, (ii) zircon in granites, and (iii) magnetite in gabbros.

Some metals, such as gold and tin (as cassiterite), were mined from alluvial deposits long before they were mined from any other type of ore deposit. This highlights some important aspects of placer deposits: they occur mostly in loose sediments, they are easily worked, and the ore minerals are easily separated. Nowadays, alluvial placer deposits are worked in bulk with high-pressure water jets. Much of the world's tin is obtained in this way at sites in Brazil and Malaysia. Beach placer deposits are also particularly appropriate for modern methods of extraction, because they can be mined in bulk by dredging (see Figure 50). Important occurrences of rutile–zircon–ilmenite sands occur in both eastern and western Australia (see box 'The 'black sand' deposits of eastern Australia' for an example).

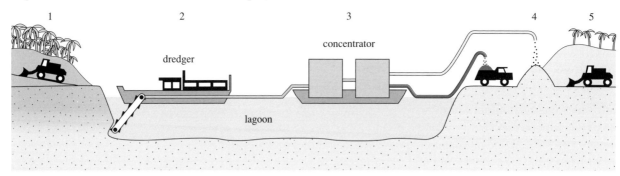

Figure 50 Mining of unconsolidated deposits such as beach placers by dredging. Working in a lagoon provides water to facilitate the transportation of material that needs only screening and sorting but not crushing; such operations are extremely flexible: 1 *preparation*—vegetation and soil are cleared from the ground to be mined; 2 *dredging*—the dredger undermines and collects heavy-mineral bearing sand; sand slurry is pumped to the concentrator; 3 *concentration*—the concentrator screens the sand and separates heavy minerals from the slurry; heavy mineral concentrate is shipped for processing; 4 *stacking*—waste sand is stacked up; 5 *rehabilitation*—trees are planted to hold the sand in place and re-establish natural habitats.

'*Fossil*' placer deposits—that is, placer deposits that have been buried and consolidated since their initial accumulation—are few in number, but some have proved to be of immense value. The best known is the Witwatersrand Goldfield in South Africa, which has provided over 50% of the world's gold (as well as much silver and uranium) since mining started at the end of the nineteenth century, and ranks as one of the world's most valuable ore deposits. Another is the Elliot Lake district in Ontario, Canada, which is one of the world's largest sources of uranium ore. Both of these deposits are Precambrian in age and occur in coarse-grained sedimentary rocks (conglomerates), which were probably deposited in river deltas.

Question 25 _____

Using the SADE approach to help you, discuss the main factors that led to the formation of the 'black sand' beach placer deposits of eastern Australia.

The 'black sand' deposits of eastern Australia

Though they are not among the largest placer deposits in the world, the black sands of North Stradbroke Island off the eastern coast of Australia provide a particularly clear example of the formation of beach placer deposits. The geography of the island is shown in Figure 51a. A long, sandy beach borders the eastern margin of the island, and is separated by a swamp from the main part of the island, where sand dunes rise to a height of more than 200 m.

The accumulation of the black sands is due to summer storms, which blow on to the island from the southeast. In this high-energy environment, sand is moved along the shore by incoming waves to form a storm beach. The turbulence of the wave action stirs the sand; lighter quartz grains are returned to the sea in the backwash, leaving the dense minerals on the storm beach. This is one form of winnowing action. Another occurs at low tide, when onshore winds blow light sand from the lower beach to cover and preserve storm beaches with dunes (see cross-section, Figure 51b). During periods of exceptionally strong winds, sand from these near-shore dunes is blown even further westwards and is added to the high dunes in the centre of the island. Sorting by wave action is most efficient and produces the highest-grade heavy mineral deposits. Wind action is less efficient at sorting than water, but tends to transport the lighter quartz grains more readily than the heavy minerals.

Zircon, rutile and ilmenite are the main ore minerals, but monazite, although in tiny amounts, is another valuable component. These heavy minerals are most abundant in the storm beaches, though they only occur in small tonnages. Higher tonnages of lower-grade ore are available from the near-shore dunes and the high dunes. The estimated resources (before mining began) were as follows:

location	quantity of ore (sand)/t	grade of heavy minerals/%
storm beach	3 000	12
near-shore dunes	2 million	8
high dunes	400 million	1.7

The ultimate source of the sand is not certain but is thought to be the crystalline rocks, such as granites and basalts, of the interior of Australia. Their weathering products were carried to the sea by rivers and then diverted northwards along the shore by the prevailing wave and current action.

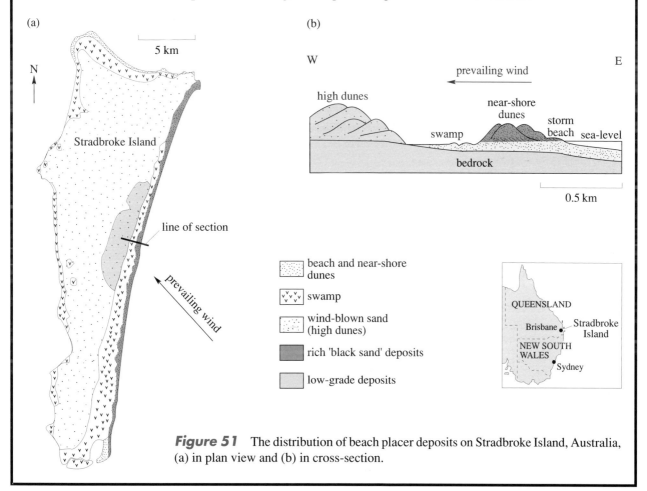

(a)

(b)

Figure 51   The distribution of beach placer deposits on Stradbroke Island, Australia, (a) in plan view and (b) in cross-section.

3.5 Summary of Section 3

1   Processes at the Earth's surface, in addition to forming deposits of bulk resources — particularly industrial minerals — can also concentrate metals to form ore deposits. Minerals resistant to weathering are concentrated by physical transport and deposition to form placer deposits. Chemical processes concentrate metals through removal of soluble material to leave behind residual deposits, and by precipitation of dissolved material in a variety of different environments, to form bedded sedimentary deposits and encrusted deposits under water, and secondary enrichment deposits beneath the land surface.

2   Chemical transport and precipitation of metals in surface and near-surface waters are controlled largely by changes in the pH and/or the oxidizing conditions of the environment. These conditions are often influenced by the reducing properties of decaying organic matter. Percolating groundwater starts off as oxidizing and slightly acidic due to dissolved atmospheric gases in rainwater. With progressive seepage, reactions with rocks and organic matter change the pH and make the groundwater more reducing.

3   Residual deposits are the insoluble residues that result from intense weathering of surface rocks in tropical climates where rainfall is high and intermittent, but drainage is good, erosion is minimal, and soils dry out regularly. Lateritic soils rich in insoluble oxides of iron and aluminium are a common form of residual deposit. Sometimes they contain ore deposits of nickel, cobalt, copper and gold, which are minable to quite low grades because they are easily accessible and poorly consolidated. The most important form of laterite is bauxite, the ore of aluminium, which is composed largely of hydrated aluminium oxides. The best sources of bauxite are rocks accessible to percolating rainwater and low in other metals, such as iron and titanium, which also form insoluble weathering products but are undesirable as impurities in the ore. Under warm, humid climatic conditions, silica produced during chemical weathering is more soluble than alumina in surface waters.

4   Weathering of mineral deposits by oxidizing rainwater often leads to the formation of secondary enrichment deposits. Metals such as copper and silver may be leached from sulphide minerals under oxidizing conditions at and near the Earth's surface, often leaving an oxidized deposit of hydrated iron(III) oxide as a leached capping or gossan. The metal-rich solutions migrate downwards to the water table, where they may react with primary ore minerals under reducing conditions to form metal-enriched secondary ore minerals. Secondary enrichment zones are particularly important in dispersed porphyry ore deposits.

5   Chemical (or biochemical) precipitation in shallow seas was responsible for deposition of Precambrian BIF and more recent (Jurassic) ironstones, which form extensive iron-rich deposits. The ultimate source of iron is not always clear: it is most likely to have been transported as Fe^{2+} ions either in solution or attached to organic colloids. Economic grades currently exceeding 60% iron in many BIF deposits have usually been enhanced by leaching and secondary enrichment processes.

6   Manganese nodules form slowly on the floors of deep oceans by precipitation of hydrated iron(III) and manganese(IV) oxides in layers. They also contain relatively high levels of nickel, copper and cobalt, along with zinc and lead, reaching a combined abundance of 3% in some parts of the oceans. Thus, manganese nodules are a potential resource for

these metals if problems of extraction, ownership and environmental damage can be resolved; they are currently a conditional resource.

7   Placer deposits are concentrations of hard, dense, chemically stable minerals which are liberated by chemical breakdown and erosion of source rocks. These heavy minerals are physically concentrated through transport in surface waters and subsequent deposition, to form alluvial deposits in rivers and beach deposits along coasts. The main minerals recovered are gold and cassiterite (SnO_2) from alluvial deposits, and heavy oxide minerals such as rutile (TiO_2) and ilmenite ($FeTiO_3$) from beach deposits. Some 'fossil' placer deposits of Precambrian age are among the world's most important gold and uranium deposits. Recent, unconsolidated placer deposits are easy to mine by dredging or with high-pressure water jets.

4 ORE DEPOSITS FORMED BY HYDROTHERMAL PROCESSES

Hydrothermal ores are probably the most widespread and diverse of all ore deposits. They have had great historical significance because they often form easily recognizable, conveniently accessible, and highly concentrated deposits, well suited to small-scale extraction. Most of the ore deposits that have been worked in the UK are of hydrothermal origin. Their minerals are probably familiar to anyone who has sifted through old mine dumps in the Pennines, Wales, the Lake District, south-west England and parts of Scotland, where crystalline masses of galena (PbS), sphalerite (ZnS), pyrite (FeS_2), chalcopyrite ($CuFeS_2$) and barite ($BaSO_4$) may be found (Plates 65 and 66). These minerals were mainly extracted from veins similar to that shown in Figure 52a, but developed on a larger scale. So, what is it about hydrothermal ores that distinguishes them from other types of ore deposit?

The most essential part of an active **hydrothermal system** is the hydrothermal fluid, which is basically hot water occupying pores and fissures within the Earth's crust and visible only where it escapes at the Earth's surface. You have already seen in Video Band 13: *Renewable Energy* that such hydrothermal fluids can be intercepted at considerable depth and tapped for their heat by geothermal wells. If released, they may emerge under pressure as jets of hot water and steam, rather like the natural geyser illustrated in Plate 67. Video Band 13 also reveals how readily these cooling and outgassing hydrothermal fluids can deposit calcium carbonate in pipes, showing that they often contain dissolved material that can be precipitated out as minerals.

(a)

(b)

(c)

Figure 52 Forms of hydrothermal vein deposits:
(a) mineral vein with dark arsenopyrite along the margins and white quartz in the centre; (b) fractured mudstone with calcite veining; blocks of rock have been separated during fracturing and the space filled in by deposition of calcite; (c) brecciated mudstone with calcite veining; blocks of rock have been fragmented during fracturing to form a fault breccia; the space between fragments of rock is filled with calcite.

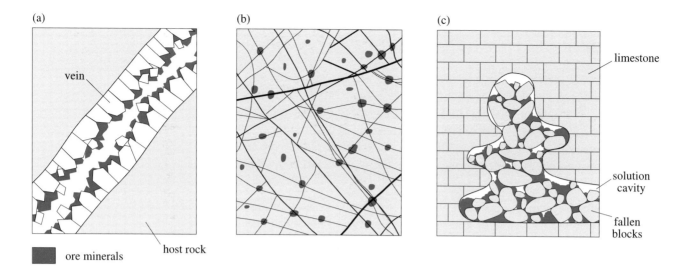

(a)

vein

host rock

ore minerals

(b)

(c)

limestone

solution cavity

fallen blocks

Figure 53 Typical forms of hydrothermal mineralization: (a) a simple vein (sometimes open at the centre), formed by mineral deposition in a fissure, may become more complex and banded with periodic enlargement as the minerals deposited can change with time (Plate 65); (b) disseminated mineralization in fractures of a stockwork, and in surrounding altered rock; (c) solution cavities in limestone containing pockets of ore minerals as replacement deposits.

Hydrothermal deposits are the solid products of a hydrothermal system. They may include ore minerals, such as those noted above, but more commonly they consist of worthless minerals, such as calcite or quartz. Quartz veins are commonly found in metamorphic rocks, and calcite veins are frequently associated with limestones. Either may be indicative of hydrothermal activity, but they are mostly **barren** (unmineralized). Hydrothermal deposits may be found in crustal rocks wherever cooling hydrothermal fluids have gained access, forming vein deposits in open fractures, disseminated deposits in permeable rocks, and replacement deposits in soluble rocks. Schematic examples of these occurrences are illustrated in Figure 53. The complexity of some vein deposits is shown on a small scale in Figure 52b and c. Fluids escaping from the crust produce encrusted deposits as chimneys around vents under water (black smokers — Block 1, Section 3.6.4), and mounds or terraces where fluids escape onto the land surface as geysers or hot springs (Plate 67).

So how do hydrothermal ore deposits form? Ore deposits formed in igneous and sedimentary environments (as considered in Sections 2 and 3) are generally easy to understand because the processes involved in their formation are directly comparable with those that form igneous and sedimentary rocks. But as we don't normally consider *hydrothermal rocks* as a separate category, the processes that lead to the formation of hydrothermal deposits are not as familiar. However, we have already examined the formation of porphyry ore deposits (Section 2.4), in association with igneous processes, and secondary enrichment deposits (Section 3.2.2), by surface processes, in both of which ore minerals are deposited from aqueous solutions within the Earth's crust.

○ Which of these might we consider to be a hydrothermal deposit?

○ The porphyry ore deposits. Because they involve precipitation of ore minerals from *hot*, aqueous solutions derived either from a magma body or from its surrounding rocks, they can be regarded as hydrothermal deposits. Secondary enrichment involves dissolution and reprecipitation of metals by *cool* groundwater (which cannot be described as hydrothermal) in the near-surface environment.

Before examining ore deposits formed by hydrothermal systems in more detail, we shall look at the basic principles by which hydrothermal systems work, and in particular, what makes them capable of forming ore deposits.

4.1 The anatomy of a hydrothermal system

A hydrothermal system has several essential parts, which can be linked directly to the aspects of 'SADE' that help us to explain ore deposit form-ation (Section 1.5). Here, as suggested earlier, we extend the mnemonic to 'SPADE' because *Pathways* are of great importance in hydrothermal systems. However, we shall also change the order in which we discuss the aspects to 'ASPED' so that they fit more closely with the logical development of a hydrothermal system.

The most essential part of a mineralizing hydrothermal system is the supply of a hot watery solution, or hydrothermal fluid, the *Agent*, which requires access to *Sources*, the geochemical reservoirs from which metals can be leached. In order to migrate and transport dissolved material through fissures or permeable rock *Pathways*, the agent requires geothermal heat *Energy*, both to promote chemical reactions and to drive convection. Eventually, if the agent experiences appropriate physical and/or chemical changes and space is available, *Deposition* of hydrothermal minerals will occur. These aspects of SPADE are described in more detail below.

4.1.1 Structural aspects of a hydrothermal system

The generalized form of a hydrothermal system is shown in Figure 54, in which important physical and chemical aspects of the system are identified. This Section deals mainly with *physical* aspects of this generalized system in the context of 'SPADE'.

Agent—the waters that become hydrothermal fluids

Water occurs in crustal rocks in several different forms (Figure 54):

* *meteoric water* is derived from rainfall, is low in dissolved constituents, and enters rocks by infiltration;

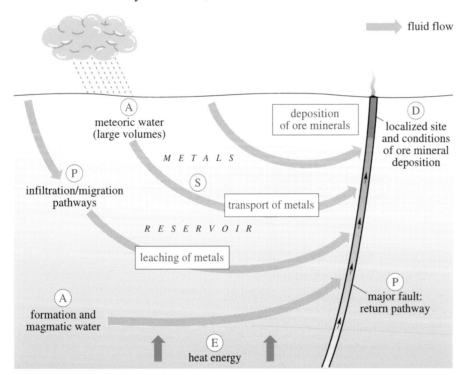

Figure 54 The anatomy of a hydrothermal system in schematic form. Physical aspects are ascribed to their role according to SPADE—*Sources* (S), *Pathways* (P), *Agents* (A), *Deposition* (D) and *Energy* (E). Chemical processes are shown in boxed text. Grey arrows show the flow path of aqueous solutions (hydrothermal fluids).

- *seawater* occupies the oceans, is saline, containing about 3.5% of dissolved constituents (mainly Na^+, K^+, Mg^{2+}, Ca^{2+}, Cl^- and SO_4^{2-}), and may enter rocks either by infiltration or as formation water when trapped in the pores of marine sediments;
- *magmatic water* is expelled from magmas and may contain as much as 20–25% of dissolved constituents.

Only magmatic waters are likely to start out with very high concentrations of trace metals. Separation of water from a magma happens in a very reactive environment, and many metals preferentially enter the aqueous solution as it separates from the magma, as noted in Section 2.4. Other forms of hydrothermal solution only gain such high concentrations of metals through dissolution or breakdown of existing minerals and leaching of rocks (Section 1.5). In general, the richer the chemical cocktail that a hydrothermal solution contains, the more reactive it is likely to be; so compared to meteoric water, seawater has a head start and magmatic fluids are generally the most reactive. Hydrothermal fluids may originate from any of these sources or from a mixture of sources. Although magmatic water may be available in areas of igneous activity, hot springs in volcanic regions on land may be entirely of meteoric origin, whereas the waters circulating through the upper layers of oceanic crust are dominated by seawater (Block 1, Section 3.6.4).

To maintain a hydrothermal system, a static accumulation of water is not enough; there must be a continual supply of water to feed it (Figure 54), and that requires *movement* of water.

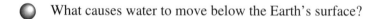 What causes water to move below the Earth's surface?

It flows under gravity, it convects when heated, and it can be squeezed out of pores in rocks on compaction.

Infiltrating water flows under *gravity* to the water table, the level below which an aquifer is saturated in water. Further movement may occur through leakage from the aquifer, which may be via springs. This movement is driven by the head of water pressure between the spring opening and the level of the water table (as described in Block 3). The same mechanism supplies groundwater to the hot springs of Bath (see box overleaf). Another important mechanism of movement is *convection*, whereby water heated by hot rocks expands, its density decreases, and it becomes buoyant as the surrounding cooler, denser water displaces it. As the cooler water is heated, it rises and is itself displaced, so forming a circulating convection system. This is the basis of the geothermal energy systems featured in Block 4 Part 2. The effect of *compaction* is to expel formation waters from a subsiding pile of wet, clay-rich sedimentary rocks when they are compressed on burial by overlying sediments. Similar processes have been described in Block 4 Part 1, linked to the migration of hydrocarbons.

Sources — the reservoirs supplying ore mineral constituents

Any rocks accessible to hydrothermal fluids are potential source rocks for metals that may eventually form ore deposits (Figure 54). If these rocks contain metals in a leachable form, which can be readily extracted by hydrothermal fluids, the rocks can be described as **fertile**. In shales, especially black shales (Section 3.3), ions of certain metals (such as Cu, Zn, Pb, U and Mo) are often rather loosely attached to organic material and clay minerals, and may be released into solution and expelled with saline formation water. In addition, reactive hydrothermal fluids may react with minerals in the rocks they pass through, leaching or exchanging metal ions with the host rock.

Hot springs of Bath

If groundwater passes through relatively hot, permeable rocks before it escapes at the surface, it heats up. Water that feeds springs in volcanic areas is often heated in this way, forming hot springs as a result. The tapping of heat from such sources in New Zealand and Italy was described in Block 4 Part 2. However, it is not necessary to go to a volcanic region to find hot springs. For example, the town of Bath has been known for its hot springs since Roman times.

There are several locations in the Bath area where water emerges from the ground at temperatures of 40–50 °C. As at many other places where naturally warm waters are found, the popular belief that these waters could alleviate a range of medical conditions grew and was of great importance in the development of the town in the eighteenth and nineteenth centuries. The sites of the springs on which bathing pools had been built were not studied in detail until 1977, when a fatality occurred due to an infection caused by a form of amoeba that had taken up residence in the warm oxidizing waters of the surface pools. These studies showed that the hot waters rise through gravels, which fill funnel-shaped hollows in the underlying Jurassic clays. At depth, under reducing conditions, the waters were free of the organism, and direct access to these sources via boreholes has made the thermal waters of Bath safe once again.

How are these waters heated and their supply maintained? Figure 55 shows the geological setting of the Bath area and the movement of groundwater. An important feature is the Carboniferous limestone aquifer, which is down-folded so that it dips from its outcrop in the Mendips to reach depths of 2.5 km before rising to just beneath the surface at Bath, where it is overlain by Jurassic limestones and clays. Under a normal geothermal gradient of about 20–25 °C km^{-1}, the limestone rocks at their deepest are quite hot, perhaps 70–90 °C. Water collecting as rainfall on the Mendip Hills, where the water table maintains a head of pressure, flows along the permeable limestone aquifer and is heated to that temperature. Faults beneath Bath enable the hot water to rise rapidly under pressure without mixing with cooler, high-level groundwaters, so allowing the water to retain much of its heat. Eventually it emerges at about 45 °C as the hot springs of Bath.

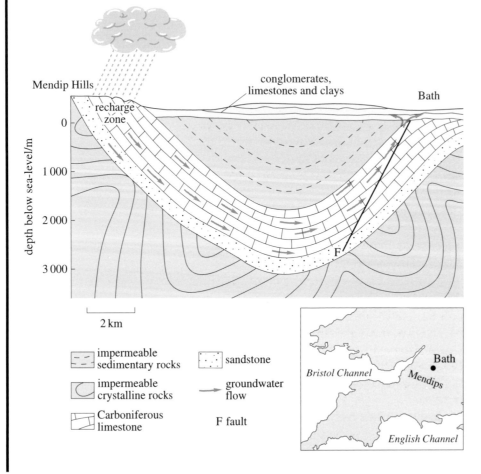

Figure 55 Simplified geological cross-section of the Bath area, showing the origin and flow path of the thermal waters. Note the exaggerated depth scale.

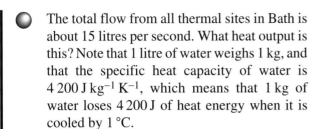 The total flow from all thermal sites in Bath is about 15 litres per second. What heat output is this? Note that 1 litre of water weighs 1 kg, and that the specific heat capacity of water is 4 200 J kg^{-1} K^{-1}, which means that 1 kg of water loses 4 200 J of heat energy when it is cooled by 1 °C.

○ Assuming a surface temperature of 15 °C, the temperature difference is 45 − 15 = 30 °C. Therefore, the heat output is

$$4\,200 \times 15 \times 30 = 1\,890\,000\,\text{J s}^{-1} = 1\,890\,\text{kW}$$
$$(1\,\text{kW} = 1\,000\,\text{J s}^{-1})$$

The time taken for the water to travel from its source in the Mendips to Bath has been evaluated by several methods, but there is still great uncertainty. It is likely that most of the supply takes from a few hundreds of years to a few thousands of years to travel through the aquifer, but there are likely to be many different routes. The most striking features of the springs are the bubbling gases (mainly nitrogen and carbon dioxide) that escape from solution as the pressure is released, and the formation of rust-coloured encrustations of hydrated iron(III) oxide (see Plate 68). The main dissolved anions are sulphate, chloride and bicarbonate; the cations are principally sodium and calcium, and in total they amount to several thousand milligrams per litre. Surprisingly, the iron content is less than 1 mg l^{-1}, present as Fe^{2+}(aq) in the mildly acidic (pH 6.5–6.7), reducing water until it reaches the surface, where it is oxidized and precipitates as hydrated iron(III) oxide.

Rocks that cannot easily supply metals to a hydrothermal fluid are called **infertile.** (*Note* We describe potential source rocks as *infertile* if they cannot supply metals, and rocks or veins as *barren* if they are not mineralized.) An example of an infertile rock is sandstone, especially quartzite, which is composed almost entirely of silica (SiO$_2$) with few impurities (trace metals). Rocks that either contain very stable (inert) minerals or have already been scavenged by hydrothermal fluids and are thus depleted in trace metals can also be described as infertile. We shall see repeatedly in Sections 4.2 and 4.3 that the mineralogy and chemistry of source rocks (their *fertility*) exert an important control on the availability of metals and hence on the diverse types of ore deposit that may be formed in hydrothermal systems, even when the *processes* involved in their formation are essentially the same.

For magma-derived hydrothermal fluids the metals reservoir is primarily the magma itself (as described for porphyry deposits in Section 2.4). In this case, the availability of metals depends on the composition of the magma and the competition for metals between crystallizing minerals, the magma remaining and the separated aqueous fluid.

Pathways—access for fluids to fertile source rocks and routes to a site of deposition

Pore space and cavities in rocks may contain groundwater and hydrothermal fluids, but, just as for water supply and for migration of hydrocarbons, these spaces must be connected for movement of the fluid to occur (Figure 54). Permeable pathways may be provided by rock formations with connected pores or well-developed joint systems — such as sandstone and limestone, respectively — by volcanic ashes, and by fracture systems. In impermeable rocks, such as shales or igneous rocks, flow of fluids is concentrated along fractures and joints, which open up when flexing of the crust occurs at times of tectonic activity. Fracturing may also be related to local events, such as magma intrusion and explosive boiling of hydrothermal solutions on their way to the surface (recall Figure 33), or to larger-scale crustal movements associated with tectonic activity, often near plate boundaries.

○ Why is repeated opening of fractures important for the formation of hydrothermal vein deposits?

Hydrothermal systems require pathways to supply fluids and transport metals. For continuing fluid flow and deposition of minerals, these pathways must be open. However, as a result of deposition, fractures often seal themselves, which prevents the movement of fluids and further deposition. Thus, repeated opening of fractures by tectonic stresses is necessary to maintain open pathways, and plays an important role in extending the lifetimes of hydrothermal systems.

The form of many hydrothermal veins, involving mineral zonation parallel to the margins (such as in Plate 65) — and often symmetrically distributed about a central zone (sometimes with open spaces or cavities) as in Figures 52a and 53a — indicates repeated or prolonged opening of fractures and reflects deposition from fluids with changing compositions.

Pathways are needed to provide fluids with access to large quantities of rock as sources of mineralizing components, with channels for transporting those components in solution, and for focusing fluids into a localized zone for deposition (Figure 54).

Energy — the driving force

Heat not only drives a hydrothermal system by causing convection in the hydrothermal fluid, but high-temperature fluids can carry high concentrations of material in solution, which makes them more likely to react with minerals, and leads to the alteration and replacement of minerals in surrounding rocks.

Geothermal heat is supplied to a hydrothermal fluid from surrounding rocks, which become progressively hotter with depth. This variation in temperature, the *geothermal gradient*, is developed because the Earth cools from its surface and is heated internally by natural radioactivity. The depth at which a particular temperature is reached, however, varies from place to place. In a stable tectonic setting, in the interior of a continent, with a normal geothermal gradient, temperatures may reach only 250 °C at 10 km depth, but in an active volcanic area, where hot magma is injected towards the surface, gradients can be much higher, and temperatures of 250 °C or more can be encountered within a kilometre or two of the surface.

Convection also plays an important role in focusing large volumes of fluids through channels to localized sites of mineral deposition (Figure 54). The buoyancy of heated water provides the driving force for convection. Hot water rises wherever there is an easy escape route, such as a deep fault (see, for example, Figure 55), which can act as a constrained pathway to focus fluid flow so that it arrives at a localized site where deposition of minerals can occur. The form of a convecting hydrothermal system, therefore, may be controlled by the location of permeable (faulted) pathways, especially where fluids are heated in a laterally uniform geothermal gradient (Figure 54). A localized heat source (and therefore a laterally variable geothermal gradient) could also focus fluids by convection.

Deposition — the site and conditions for ore minerals to accumulate

Without *pathways* (connected space) for hydrothermal fluids to flow through, and open space for ore minerals to crystallize in, ore deposits could not form. Therefore, the availability of *space* at potential sites of deposition (Figure 54) is critical in determining the *form* of an ore deposit. *Dispersed deposits* (Section 1.3), which consist of small grains, pockets or veins of ore minerals dispersed through a body of rock (as in Figure 53b), are usually associated with low-grade ores and depend on diffuse fluid flow through the rock, with only small amounts of available space. *Confined deposits* are usually concentrations of ore minerals, often occurring as veins (Figure 53a), which follow geological features — a sedimentary layer or a fault — or even occupy cavities dissolved out of limestone (Figure 53c). The form of a deposit is also dependent on whether the site is on or below the Earth's surface, and, if on the surface, whether it is on land or in a submarine environment.

Changes in conditions which bring about deposition of ore minerals are discussed further in Section 4.1.2. In physical terms, hot fluids cool as they pass through rocks at higher levels in the crust, and may even mix with cooler, near-surface fluids. With reduction in pressure, as discussed in Section 2.4, gases may be released. Such events affect the chemistry of the fluid; as a result, deposition from hydrothermal fluids usually occurs at relatively high levels in the crust (Figure 54). On escaping from the Earth's crust on land or under water, fluids experience changes in physical (and chemical) conditions, which may lead to further precipitation of minerals.

Question 26

Given a supply of hydrothermal fluid, say whether or not each of the following could be a site where you would expect to find hydrothermal ore deposits, and why?

(i)   within the base of a thick pile of compacted shales;

(ii) in fractures in rocks overlying a granite pluton;

(iii) in well-jointed limestone.

Chemical aspects of SPADE

We have now reviewed the *physical* aspects of hydrothermal systems in the context of SPADE to set out a structural framework (Figure 54) in which hydrothermal deposits *may* form. In reality, they link closely to *chemically* controlled processes involving the fluid and its surroundings, which are *essential* requirements for hydrothermal ore deposit formation (Figure 54). They include:

(i)   *leaching* by hydrothermal fluids of ore-forming constituents (metals and anions, such as sulphide) from suitable reservoir rocks;

(ii) *transportation* of soluble ore-forming constituents in the hydrothermal fluid from a source reservoir to a site of deposition;

(iii) *deposition* of ore minerals by precipitation from the hydrothermal fluid where physical or chemical conditions change.

⬤   Use Figure 54 to help establish which aspects of SPADE are involved in each of these three processes?

◯   (i)   *Leaching* involves a fluid Agent, Source rocks and heat Energy to promote chemical reactions.

   (ii) *Transportation* involves a fluid Agent, Pathways and Energy for movement of the fluid.

   (iii) *Deposition* involves a fluid Agent once again, a site of Deposition, suitable conditions for Deposition to occur, and Energy to maintain the supply of fluid.

The next Section will concentrate on fluid compositions and solution chemistry, which should assist your understanding of how these processes lead to ore formation.

4.1.2 Hydrothermal fluid compositions

How can we find out more about the composition of hydrothermal fluids? Well, they sometimes emerge at the Earth's surface as geysers and hot springs, and we can sample them. But how can they be distinguished from near-surface circulations of meteoric water, which might be hot and rich in silica or calcium carbonate, but might not be representative of deeper hydrothermal circulations or mineralizing systems? In recent years, with the investigation of active geothermal systems for their geothermal potential (Block 4 Part 2), hydrothermal fluids have been intercepted and sampled in deep boreholes at many localities. The compositions of two contrasting examples of hydrothermal waters, one from a geothermal well near the Salton Sea in California and the other from a well in the Broadlands geothermal field in New Zealand, are compared in Table 18. Alongside them are the compositions of seawater and an ancient hydrothermal fluid. Most hydrothermal fluids turn out to be saline solutions or *brines*, rich in alkali metal and chloride ions, with lesser amounts of metals such as Mg, Fe, Pb, Zn, Au and Ag, and dissolved gases such as hydrogen sulphide (H_2S), carbon dioxide (CO_2) and methane (CH_4).

To help you appreciate the differences between the modern hydrothermal fluids from Broadlands and the Salton Sea, and how they compare with seawater, answer Question 27 using Table 18.

Question 27 _____

(a) Which three metals are the most concentrated in the Salton Sea brine and how do their concentrations compare with seawater?

(b) Which metals in the Salton Sea brine have concentrations more than 1 000 times those of seawater?

(c) How would you describe the Salton Sea brine, given that seawater could be described as a saline solution, low in trace metals, and somewhat alkaline (pH 8.2)?

(d) How would you similarly describe the composition of the Broadlands fluid? Is it as saline as seawater?

(e) On compositional grounds, would fluids from Broadlands or the Salton Sea be more suitable for supplying a geothermal plant?

Question 27 and Table 18 demonstrate that the compositions of the fluids from the Broadlands and the Salton Sea geothermal systems are very different. Before we explain why the Salton Sea fluid is so much more saline than seawater, and yet the Broadlands water is much less saline than seawater, let's consider whether either the Salton Sea fluid or the Broadlands fluid could represent ore-producing hydrothermal fluids.

The only way to link a fluid to a specific type of ore deposit is to sample the fluid associated with it. But that is not easy, because most deposits that we can sample are no longer part of an active hydrothermal system. However, within many hydrothermal minerals there are pockets of fluid that were trapped during crystallization. These are called **fluid inclusions** (see box on p. 106). They can tell us about the temperature at which the host mineral crystallized and the composition of the hydrothermal fluid from which it was deposited — essential information for trying to understand how mineral deposits were formed. In Table 18, the ancient hydrothermal fluid from a fluid inclusion in fluorite, a common gangue mineral, has a high salinity, and a composition much closer to the Salton Sea fluid than seawater.

Salton Sea — modern hydrothermal fluids

One of the first major discoveries of metal-rich fluids deep in the Earth's crust took place in 1962 during exploratory drilling for geothermal power on the Colorado River delta near the edge of the Salton Sea, a large brackish water lake about 70 m below sea-level in southern California (Figure 56). This location lies on an extension of the San Andreas Fault, within a thermally active zone of crust at the northern extension of the East Pacific Rise.

One of the boreholes reached a depth of 1.6 km and tapped a highly saline hydrothermal brine at a temperature of 300–350 °C. Surprisingly, this solution contained 25% of dissolved salts compared with only 3.5% in seawater (Table 18), including very large amounts of Na^+, K^+, Ca^{2+} and Cl^- ions, as well as many other metals at concentrations far in excess of those in seawater. The mineralizing potential of the fluid was dramatically illustrated by the formation of a deposit of silica, containing fine-grained metal sulphides with an overall composition of 20% copper, 7% silver and 7% iron. These deposits accumulated at the surface at a rate of more than a tonne per month. However, zinc, lead and manganese concentrations were low in the deposits, despite the unusually high concentrations in the brine (Table 18). The Salton

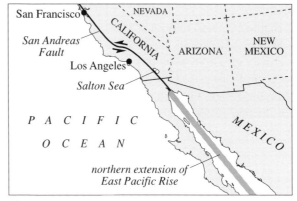

Figure 56 Geographical setting of the Salton Sea.

Sea geothermal field is still under development as a power source. It is estimated that mineral recovery from a 1 000 MW power plant on the site could provide as much as 20% of the manganese requirements for the United States.

The Salton Sea brine was originally meteoric water which percolated through evaporites bordering the Salton Sea and dissolved alkali metal chlorides. This reactive fluid then leached trace metals from buried shales that were enriched in metals (Section 3.3) to produce the metal-rich fluid with the composition given in Table 18.

Table 18 Compositions of natural waters: seawater, modern hydrothermal fluids from Broadlands and the Salton Sea, and an ancient hydrothermal fluid from a fluid inclusion in fluorite

Ions	Concentration in seawater/mg l^{-1}	Concentration in modern hydrothermal fluids/mg l^{-1}		Concentration in ancient hydrothermal fluid/mg l^{-1}
		Broadlands	Salton Sea	
Na^+	10 500	980	50 400	40 400
K^+	380	200	17 500	3 500
Ca^{2+}	400	2.4	28 000	8 600
Mg^{2+}	1 290	0.02	54	5 600
Fe^{2+}	0.002	—	2 290	—
Mn^{2+}	0.002	—	1 400	450
Cu^{2+}	0.003	—	8	9 100
Pb^{2+}	0.000 3	—	102	—
Zn^{2+}	0.005	—	540	10 900
Ba^{2+}	0.02	—	235	—
Sr^{2+}	8	—	400	—
Rb^+	0.12	2.2	135	—
Li^+	0.18	12.6	215	—
Ag^+	0.000 04	—	1.4	—
SO_4^{2-}	2 650	6.5	5	1 200
Cl^-	19 500	1 668	155 000	87 000
S^{2-}(as H_2S)	—	—	16	—
Totals	34 400	≈3 000	≈250 000	≈167 000
pH	about 8.2	8.6	6.0	—

Fluid inclusions — microsampling of hydrothermal fluids

Most fluid inclusions are quite small (only 2–20 μm in diameter), and require a powerful microscope to be seen. They look like bubbles and are visible only in transparent mineral grains. The spectacular example illustrated in Figure 57 contains not just a *liquid* but also a *crystal* and a bubble of *gas* (vapour). How did this inclusion become so complicated?

At the time of trapping, the fluid was hot and homogeneous. It did not contain either solid particles or gas bubbles. On cooling, the trapped liquid contracted much more than the mineral surrounding it. The liquid could no longer fill the pocket completely, so a space was formed, occupied by the vapour bubble. During cooling, the solubility of any dissolved salts decreased, and crystallization occurred due to the high initial concentration of salts; hence the crystal of halite (NaCl) in Figure 57.

A whole branch of science has grown up to measure and interpret the compositions of fluid inclusions. By heating an inclusion until the liquid has redissolved the salt crystal and has expanded to consume its own vapour bubble, the inclusion can be returned to the temperature at which trapping originally occurred. Temperatures of inclusion fluids estimated in this way from different types of hydrothermal system range from about 600 °C down to near-surface temperatures of about 50 °C. Inclusion fluids also

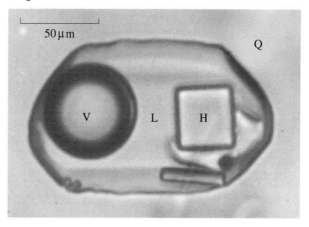

Figure 57 An inclusion of saline fluid (L) trapped in a crystal of quartz (Q) as it grew in a hydrothermal vein. The round bubble of vapour (V) and the cubic crystal of halite (H) formed on cooling.

vary greatly in their composition, and may even contain hydrocarbons — which can be of great value for exploration in the petroleum industry.

An example of the composition of a fluid inclusion is given in Table 18 for comparison with Salton Sea brine. It, too, contains high levels of dissolved salts, almost 17% in total, with sodium and chloride ions again dominant. In fact, the compositions of fluid inclusions turn out to be just as variable as those of geothermal brines.

So how do the hydrothermal fluids of the Salton Sea become so rich in dissolved material, even compared with seawater? We learned in Section 1.5 that hot solutions, particularly those already rich in salts, can be very corrosive, capable of dissolving and reacting with minerals, so increasing their metal content even further. A simple way for meteoric (almost pure) water to become saline is to percolate through evaporite deposits rich in soluble salts, such as alkali halides (such as halite, NaCl) and calcium sulphate (gypsum, $CaSO_4.2H_2O$). Even if these waters are cool, they can still acquire high concentrations of dissolved salts. Seawater, on the other hand, is already saline. Therefore, the metal content of a hydrothermal fluid depends not only on the starting composition of the fluid (whether meteoric or seawater), but also on its route through the crust and the composition of the rocks through which it passes.

This helps explain the contrasting compositions of the Salton Sea brine and the geothermal water at Broadlands. Both have meteoric sources, but the water at Broadlands passed mainly through volcanic rocks containing little soluble material, whereas the Salton Sea fluid gained a high concentration of salts from evaporites. The low salinity of the Broadlands water means that it is less reactive and less able to interact with available rocks. It might also be a shallower hydrothermal system, and lack the opportunity to react with rocks at high temperature and become highly enriched in metals.

○ In view of its origin, it is surprising that the Salton Sea brine has such a low concentration of sulphate (Table 18). Why might we expect it to be higher?

○ If most of its dissolved constituents were acquired from evaporites that contained gypsum, a high content of both Ca^{2+} and SO_4^{2-} ions would be expected. Indeed, the concentration of Ca^{2+} in the fluid is high ($28\,000\,mg\,l^{-1}$), but the concentration of sulphate (SO_4^{2-}) is only $5\,mg\,l^{-1}$. In fact the sulphide (S^{2-}) concentration is higher ($16\,mg\,l^{-1}$).

The reason for these very low sulphate and sulphide concentrations in the Salton Sea brine may be that the fluid has already deposited insoluble sulphides at depth, under reducing conditions. This may also account for the relatively low copper content of the fluid compared with some other trace metals. The presence of very much lower concentrations of sulphate in the Salton Sea fluid compared with seawater may also help to explain why barium and lead, which have rather insoluble sulphates, can exist at so much higher concentrations in the Salton Sea fluid than in seawater.

Notice from Table 18 that the main anions in hydrothermal solutions are usually chloride ions. Indeed, most metal chlorides (except AgCl and Hg_2Cl_2) are very soluble in hot water, which explains why many hydrothermal brines can carry large amounts of metals.

However, many of the most familiar ore minerals, such as the sulphides galena, sphalerite and chalcopyrite, are extremely insoluble substances. It is easy to see how these minerals might precipitate from solution, but more difficult to understand how Pb^{2+}, Zn^{2+} and Cu^{2+} ions could be transported together with S^{2-} ions without precipitating the sulphides from the hydro-thermal solution. — Well, perhaps they don't have to. A possible explanation might be that two solutions — one supplying metal ions, and one supplying sulphide ions — could combine and precipitate sulphide minerals on mixing. However, it would still be difficult for quantities of sulphide ions to be trans-ported without sulphide minerals being precipitated, so this explanation would seem rather implausible.

A better answer is in the mode of transport. Sulphur may be transported not as sulphide anions, S^{2-} (nor as persulphide anions, S_2^{2-}, as found in pyrite), which readily combine with metal ions and precipitate insoluble sulphide minerals; instead they may be transported as soluble ions. Under oxidizing conditions, sulphur can be transported as the sulphate ion, SO_4^{2-}, with which most metals form soluble salts (but very sparingly so for barium and lead). If reduction of SO_4^{2-} to S^{2-} occurs, due to reaction with organic material for example, sulphide minerals will precipitate out.

Another way in which sulphur and metals may be transported in solution is as metal complexes or complex ions. **Complex ions** comprise a central atom (often a metal) surrounded by anions or neutral species to form a larger group of atoms bearing their combined charge. Metals such as Ni, Cu, Zn, Pb, Pt, Hg and Au are able to form complex ions, especially with the bisulphide anion, HS^-, in reducing conditions. The resulting complex ions, such as $[Zn(HS)_3]^-$, $[PbS(HS)]^-$ and $[HgS(HS)]^-$, are often soluble, and may be transported in solution *without* precipitation of sulphide minerals. However, the presence (or stability) of such complexes depends critically on the composition of the solution and its temperature, pressure, pH and the oxidizing conditions.

Studies of active hydrothermal systems have shown that gold may be transported as either of the complex ions $[Au(HS)_2]^-$ or $[AuCl_2]^-$, depending on the conditions and fluid composition. In reducing solutions, gold may be present as the $Au^+(aq)$ ion. With a significant concentration of hydrogen sulphide (H_2S, which smells like rotten eggs) in solution, bisulphide ions (HS^-) are formed (Equation 4.1) and combine with the $Au^+(aq)$ ions to form the stable complex ion $[Au(HS)_2]^-$ (Equation 4.2):

$$H_2S(aq) = H^+(aq) + HS^-(aq) \qquad (4.1)$$

$$Au^+(aq) + 2HS^-(aq) = [Au(HS)_2]^-(aq) \qquad (4.2)$$

If confining pressure is reduced, and especially if boiling occurs, H_2S is released from solution, the complex becomes unstable and gold metal is precipitated.

Precipitation of hydrothermal minerals may take place for a number of reasons, including:

- temperature change (cooling), which may reduce the solubility of salts;
- pressure change (reduction), which may cause outgassing (release of dissolved gases) and boiling;
- chemical reaction with wall rocks and mixing with other fluids, bringing about changes in pH and/or the oxidizing condition of the fluid.

These are the main ways in which hydrothermal ore minerals are formed. The same basic processes operate in a range of circumstances to produce ore deposits, which will be examined in Sections 4.2 and 4.3.

Question 28

Why is the HS^- ion likely to be important in the formation of sulphide ore deposits?

4.1.3 The scale and duration of hydrothermal processes

It is clear that a combination of physical and chemical factors are required to form hydrothermal deposits, but to form an *ore deposit*, a hydrothermal system must be developed on a *large scale* and for a *long period of time*. Figure 54 shows schematically another very important principle of hydrothermal systems, namely that circulating hydrothermal fluids must generally pass through *large volumes* of crustal rocks in order to obtain their complement of metals, and then rise by convection, focused into fault-controlled pathways, to deposit ore minerals in a *small volume* of crust. This explains how even small concentrations of metals leached from source rocks can be sufficient to produce ore deposits at the site of deposition, providing there is enough water available to maintain the system.

So let's first consider just what *volume* of water might be required to form a hydrothermal ore deposit.

 If a hydrothermal zinc deposit contains 5 Mt of ore, with an average grade of 3% zinc, what volume of hydrothermal fluid was involved in forming the deposit, if it was capable of depositing 200 mg (milligrams) of zinc per litre of the fluid? (*Note* This is quite a lot of zinc. To put it into context, compare it with the hot spring waters of Bath, which contain only $1 \, \text{mg} \, l^{-1}$ of iron in solution, but still precipi-tate hydrated iron(III) oxide; see Plate 68.)

○ The quantity of zinc in the deposit is $5 \times 10^6 \times 0.03 = 150 \times 10^3$ t. If one litre of fluid deposits 200 mg of zinc, then the total volume of fluid required to form 150×10^3 t of zinc is

$150 \times 10^3 \times 10^6 / 0.2$ litres ($1\,t = 10^6\,g$)

$= 750 \times 10^9$ litres

$= 0.75 \times 10^9\,m^3$ (10^3 litres $= 1\,m^3$)

but, $10^9\,m^3 = 1\,km^3$, so, the volume of water is $0.75\,km^3$.

This volume of water is equivalent to a sizeable lake, which could be $100\,km^2$ in area and 7.5 m deep. Alternatively, a seepage of 7.5 cm per year over an area of $100\,km^2$ for 100 years would be sufficient. Hence, for geologically realistic times of thousands or tens of thousands of years, it wouldn't be difficult to supply enough hydrothermal fluid from a region of $10\,km \times 10\,km$ to form this size of deposit. But, of course, it would be necessary to channel all this water into a localized site of deposition. The persistence of a heat source to aid convection and structural pathways would be necessary to provide the necessary focusing of fluids over long periods of time.

Now let's consider the *size* of the source region supplying the zinc.

○ The average crustal abundance of zinc is 70 ppm, but not all of it may be in a form that is leachable. If it were possible to leach, say, an average of 25 ppm from rocks accessible to fluids, how extensive would the source region have to be?

○ To produce 150×10^3 t of zinc would require leaching of

$\dfrac{150 \times 10^3}{25 \times 10^{-6}} = 6 \times 10^9$ t of crust

Converting to volume, and assuming a crustal density of $2.75\,t\,m^{-3}$ ($= 2.75 \times 10^9\,t\,km^{-3}$), the volume of crust is

$\dfrac{6 \times 10^9}{2.75 \times 10^9}\,km^3$

that is, $\approx 2.2\,km^3$.

This volume of crustal leaching could represent a layer 22 m thick over an area of $100\,km^2$, or, alternatively, fluid pathways might need only to access about 1% of a 2.2 km thick portion of crust over an area of $10\,km \times 10\,km$.

Therefore, so long as a sufficiently *large volume* of source rock is accessible to fluids, a relatively *small percentage* of leaching may be sufficient to produce an ore deposit.

4.1.4 Summary of hydrothermal ore-forming systems

The Earth's crust contains large volumes of groundwater occupying pores and fractures in rocks. At depth, where surrounding rocks are hot, groundwater heats up and becomes a hydrothermal fluid, capable of reacting with minerals, and leaching metals from the rocks through which it passes. When heated sufficiently, and pathways are available, these fluids become buoyant enough to convect to higher levels in the crust, even to the surface as hot springs. The flow of buoyant fluid is focused by taking the easiest route to the surface, which may, for example, be through an open fissure, a brecciated fault zone, or an aquifer.

To form ore deposits, the composition, temperature, pH and oxidizing condition of the hydrothermal fluid must first be suitable to leach metals from source rocks, and then accommodate them in solution during transportation. Eventually, physical processes, such as cooling, or boiling on reduction of confining pressure, or chemical reactions with wall rocks or other fluids, may bring about changes in conditions, causing the deposition of minerals as the fluid migrates. Not all the dissolved metals may be deposited at once, and the solution need not be very concentrated in metals. The amount of material deposited depends not only on the composition of the fluid, but on the duration and rate of flow, and hence the total volume of fluid passing. Continuing activity is essential, so repeated fracturing, triggered by tectonic events may be important. In essence, if large volumes of crustal rocks are available to provide sources of metals, large volumes of water are available to transport metals, and, if fluid flow is focused at a localized site for an extended period of time, an ore deposit could well result.

Hydrothermal deposits form where suitable physical and chemical conditions allow precipitation of minerals from hydrothermal fluids. These deposits can only become ore deposits if they contain ore minerals in sufficient concentration and volume to be worth mining. The site of deposition is an important factor, not only in setting the conditions for particular ore minerals to precipitate, but also in providing the space for the deposit to form. For convenience, we can divide hydrothermal ore deposits into those formed by the escape of hydrothermal fluids *at* or *near* the Earth's surface (Section 4.2), on land or on the sea floor, and those formed well *beneath* the Earth's surface (Section 4.3) where hydrothermal fluids are expelled from compacting sediments or are convected around hot igneous intrusions. As there is probably a greater diversity of hydrothermal ore deposits than any other type, we shall only be looking at some of the more well-known types. This diversity stems mainly from the variety of rock types and settings encountered in crustal environments; but, broadly speaking, most of the *processes* involved are the same.

4.2 Surface and near-surface hydrothermal ore deposits

Hydrothermal fluids that emerge from geothermally active parts of the Earth's crust either on to the *land surface* or on to the *sea floor* are known as **exhalative**. Let's look at ways in which these two environments differ before considering the nature of the ore deposits that may form there.

○ What are the main physical differences between these environments, and how do they affect the behaviour of the fluid?

___

○ On land, hydrothermal fluid *escapes into the air*, perhaps as a geyser when under pressure, or more gently as a spring, and then flows or seeps away if it doesn't evaporate first. Dissolved material may be precipitated to form encrustations on surfaces (Plate 67). Gases and steam can escape into the atmosphere.

On escaping from the ocean floor, hydrothermal fluids *mix with cool seawater*; the change in temperature and chemical environment may bring about the precipitation of minerals to encrust surfaces or become dispersed in suspension. Under high pressure, deep in the oceans, gases may remain in solution.

Another important difference between these two environments is in the likely composition of the source rocks. The composition of continental crust (on average rather like granodiorite), which underlies thermally active zones on land, differs from that of oceanic crust (on average rather like basalt), which underlies thermally active zones of the ocean floor. Thus, the rocks with which the emerging fluids have been in contact have quite different compositions, and therefore the metals available to be scavenged are also different.

The mineralogy of oceanic crust is dominated by ferromagnesian silicate minerals, whereas the dominant silicate minerals of the continental crust are quartz, feldspars and micas. Seawater heated within the ocean floor alters ferromagnesian minerals to chlorite and clay minerals (involving breakdown reactions rather like those involved in weathering; see Section 3.1), releasing iron and trace elements such as copper, zinc and manganese (Block 1, Section 3.6.4). In continental crust, alteration of feldspars and micas is more likely to enrich fluids in barium and lead, which are trace constituents of these minerals. Thus, crustal compositions and available trace metals strongly influence the composition and mineralogy of hydrothermal deposits. The low abundance of elements such as tin, tungsten, lead, barium and silver in the basaltic rocks of the ocean floor — because they don't substitute in ferromagnesian minerals — means that these metals are generally absent from hydrothermal ore deposits in oceanic areas.

We should also think about a third difference between the land surface and the ocean floor.

⬤ How do the sources and initial compositions of groundwater differ between terrestrial and ocean-floor settings, and how effective are the hydrothermal solutions from these sources likely to be in extracting metals from the crustal rocks that they infiltrate?

⬤ On land, groundwater is meteoric — that is, derived from rainfall — and hydrothermal solutions having a meteoric origin are low in dissolved salts (initially, at least). On the ocean floor, hydrothermal solutions start out as seawater, which is saline. As saline solutions are potentially more reactive, seawater is more likely to be capable of leaching metals than low-salinity meteoric water.

4.2.1 Land-based hot spring-related deposits

Probably the most impressive evidence for active hydrothermal systems is provided by fountaining geysers, which release hot water and steam from deep within the Earth. Some of the more spectacular examples are to be found in Iceland, in the North Island of New Zealand (see Plate 67), and in Yellowstone Park, Wyoming, USA, volcanically active areas where groundwater is heated by magma chambers at relatively shallow depth. As the hot water approaches the surface, decreasing pressure may cause boiling to occur, forming steam, which provides the force for geysers to erupt. Less-active surface expressions of hydrothermal systems include hot springs, mud pools and encrusted layers forming 'frozen' terraces (Figure 58).

The main source of hot spring waters is meteoric water that has percolated deep into the crust through aquifers and fractures (as seen in the box 'Hot springs of Bath'). Such fluids may penetrate to depths of 2 km or more and attain temperatures of 200–300 °C in thermally active areas. When heated sufficiently by the hot rock, they convect back towards the surface.

(a) A geyser — hot water and steam escape under pressure.

(b) Hot springs — water escapes more gently.

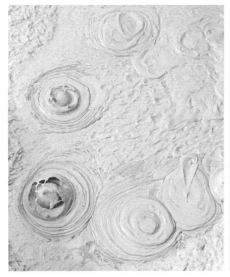

(c) Mud pools — gases (steam) bubble through hot mud.

(d) Terraces — dissolved silica (or sometimes calcium carbonate) has precipitated from cooling thermal water to form a cascade of terraces.

Figure 58 Surface expressions of hydrothermal fluids in geothermally active areas.

Redistribution of heat by these convecting fluids creates a major disturbance in underground isotherms (temperature contours) above the heat source, as shown in Figure 59. The resultant fluids are not only hot, but frequently acidic and oxidizing, and able to react with feldspars and micas to form clay minerals, an effect known as **argillic alteration** (from the Latin *argilla*, meaning clay). Notice that this effect is somewhat similar to that of surface weathering processes, as described in Section 3.1, but as hydrothermal reactions occur at depth and at higher temperatures they are likely to be more rapid. Just as with weathering reactions, the breakdown of one mineral and formation of another by alteration may release trace elements if they are not readily accommodated in the alteration products. In this way, fluids can *scavenge* soluble trace elements from the rocks they alter. The metals that can be scavenged depend on the initial rock composition and its mineralogy, as well as the temperature and composition of the fluid.

On emerging at the surface, hydrothermal solutions or brines cool rapidly, and often precipitate dissolved material to form encrusted layers or even mounds and terraces (Figure 58d and Plate 67). The most common hot spring deposits are either **sinter**, composed of precipitated silica, or travertine,

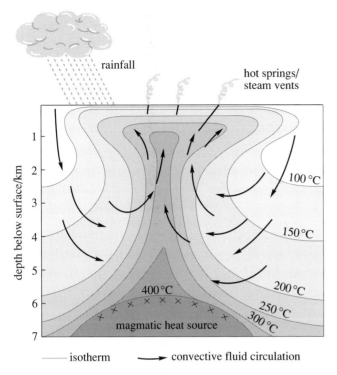

Figure 59 Hydrothermal fluid circulation feeding a hot spring system in volcanic regions where magma chambers occur at shallow depth. Convected fluids control the distribution of isotherms (temperature contours).

composed of precipitated calcium carbonate, depending on the composition of the fluid. Although some disseminated mineralization may occur in these deposits at the surface, the main site of mineralization is below ground, in the feeder channels, where rising fluids cool and may even boil as they approach the surface (see also Figure 60).

⬤ Recalling the behaviour of similar fluids in porphyry ore systems, what effect may boiling have?

⬤ Transformation of hot watery liquids to steam results in a sudden increase in volume, which can build up enough pressure to shatter rocks. As a result, hydrothermal explosion breccias are commonly associated with hot springs, geysers and sinter terraces.

As well as producing steam, boiling releases dissolved gases and causes complex ions in solution to break down, which may result in the precipitation of minerals, such as mercury, bismuth and antimony sulphides, and, sometimes, gold and silver as native metals. These metals are derived from volcanic source rocks and carried in solution as complexes such as $[AuCl_2]^-$ and $[Au(HS)_2]^-$ (as described in Section 4.1.2). Another mechanism of precipitation may be by reaction with iron(II) in solution after its release from decomposing ferromagnesian minerals in wall rocks. This would explain the association of gold with pyrite:

$$4[Au(HS)_2]^-(aq) + 4Fe^{2+}(aq) + O_2(g) = 4FeS_2(s) + 4Au(s) + 2H_2O(l) + 4H^+(aq) \quad (4.3)$$

soluble gold   iron (II)   pyrite   gold
complex   in solution

This would be a suitable place to view Video Band 14: *Gold rush in the 1990s*. Some notes are provided in the video box to clarify the origin and occurrence of the gold deposits in Nevada. After watching, test your understanding of some of the more important points made in the first 15 minutes of the video by answering Questions 29 to 31 which follow. It will probably help you to read them through quickly and have them fresh in your mind before viewing the programme. The questions and answers together will serve as a summary.

Video Band 14: Gold rush in the 1990s

Speaker

John Wright   The Open University

Bruce Braginton   Lone Tree Mine

Billy Loughlin   Independent consultant

This video band, made in 1993/4 gives us an opportunity to see some of the effects of hot spring-related hydrothermal activity in Nevada, USA, and some of the gold-bearing rocks that result. The parts of the video most relevant at this stage are the first 15 minutes, and short sections of the remainder concerning the occurrence and form of these deposits.

You will be advised to view the video again during your study of *Metals 2*, since it also covers the economics of gold mining, ore processing, prospecting and exploration.

There are several different geological environments in which hydrothermal solutions have formed gold-bearing deposits in Nevada. Figure 60 attempts to summarize these environments. The richest deposits, containing several hundred grams per tonne of gold and even more silver, are sometimes called 'Bonanza' ores, like the Comstock Lode. They are usually

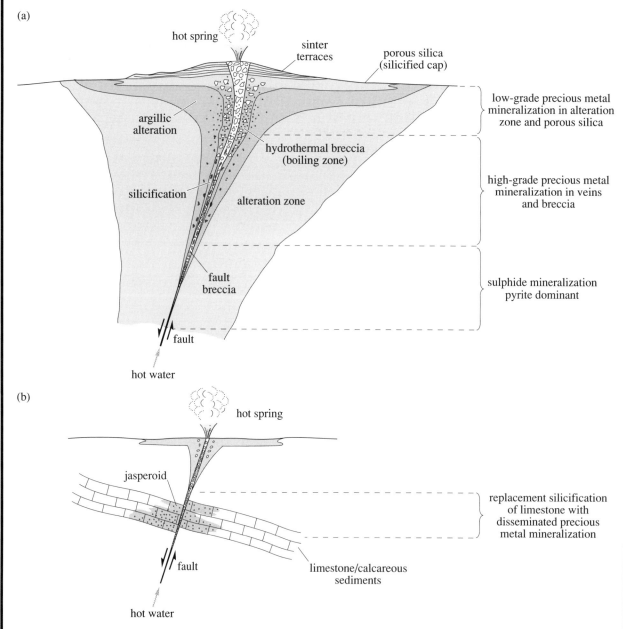

Figure 60 Diagrammatic representation of hydrothermal systems from which gold deposits have been formed in Nevada: (a) hot solutions escaping along a fault alter surrounding rocks, and deposit silica, sulphide minerals and gold in veins, fault breccias, stockwork and hydrothermal breccias; sinter terraces are formed around hot springs at the surface; (b) a hydrothermal system intersects a band of limestone, which is replaced by silica to form jasperoid. The precious metals are mainly silver and gold; their distribution is shown in colour.

found in quartz vein systems, which formed at depths of 100–350 m in feeders to hot springs, and are associated with pyrite and sulphides of the toxic elements antimony, arsenic and mercury. In the near-surface parts of hot spring systems, precious metal mineralization occurs at low grades throughout a stockwork of veins and zones of hydrothermal alteration and brecciation.

Breccias, composed of angular, broken fragments, may form by fault movements or by hydrothermal activity (as noted earlier). Faults provide major channels (pathways) for migration of hydrothermal fluids towards the surface, and sites for mineral deposition. Fault intersections are particularly favourable areas to prospect for hydrothermal deposits because of greater fluid flow and the interaction of fluids with rocks that have already been affected by earlier fluids.

Other forms of disseminated deposits mentioned during the video band are in zones of argillic alteration (Figure 60a), where fluids have penetrated and reacted with wall rocks to form clays, and in limestone (Figure 60b), where fluids have interacted with carbonates, replacing them with silica containing disseminated gold. The resulting siliceous rocks are called jasper or jasperoid when coloured red due to small amounts of iron(III) oxide. These disseminated deposits are much more extensive than vein deposits, and have become important because gold at only a few $g\,t^{-1}$ (or ppm) is economic to mine on a large scale from open pits at gold prices of about $350 per troy ounce ($11 250 per kg).

Question 29

What is the geological link between hydrothermal ore deposits and geothermal power stations? Describe in a few sentences (a) how hydrothermal ore deposits form and (b) the principle behind geothermal power stations. Base your answers on the video commentary.

Question 30

The following nine statements (a) to (g) are important points made in the video, but two are *incorrect* in one simple respect. Which are they, and why are they wrong?

(a) The Comstock Lode was formed about 12.5 million years ago; it was a mineralized zone about 6 km long and up to 300 m wide. From 1860 to 1880, virtually all the silver and gold in the Comstock Lode was mined out.

(b) Gold prospectors worked progressively downstream, so that they could locate the gold-bearing veins from which the gold grains were derived.

(c) Terraces of siliceous sinter may be formed by emerging hydrothermal fluids in the vicinity of hot springs.

(d) Strong coloration of surface rocks is an obvious sign of hydrothermal activity. Deposits containing pyrite, usually appear reddish due to decomposition on weathering to form iron(III) oxide. Hydrothermal alteration of rocks composed mostly of quartz, mica or clay under reducing conditions bleaches the rocks due to leaching of soluble iron(II).

(e) Hydrothermal solutions are highly reactive, corrosive fluids which can alter minerals and leach metals from the rocks through which they pass. As the rising fluids cool, and the confining pressure of the overlying rocks decreases, ore minerals may precipitate from solution.

(f) Breccias are good hosts for hydrothermal ore deposits because the spaces between the angular fragments make them very permeable to the passage of fluids and offer space for precipitation of ore minerals.

(g) The proliferation of gold mines in Nevada in the 1980s exploited high-grade ore deposits which became economic to mine when the price of gold rose after the fixed link between gold and money had been severed. The world-wide demand for gold then became so great, and supply so limited, that the price in January 1980 exceeded $600 per ounce, over fifteen times its price in the early 1960s.

Question 31

(a) When the early prospectors in Nevada first went panning in streams and gullies, what type of surface mineral deposit were they working and what type of deposit were they ultimately seeking?

(b) At one point in the commentary we hear that the early miners had in effect only 'half of Nevada to work in'. Bearing in mind the nature of the Basin and Range province, explain why that was.

(c) Why were the low-grade gold ores invisible to the early miners?

4.2.2 Submarine massive sulphide deposits

Submarine hydrothermal activity is usually hidden from view. Only in the last few decades has it been possible to observe and sample from hydrothermally active sites of the sea floor. Through modern deep-sea exploration, we now know much more about submarine hydrothermal systems and how exhalative deposits are formed there. Observations at mid-ocean ridge sites in the late 1970s revealed active vents (openings) in the sea floor, from which hydrothermal fluids were pouring. When these fluids, emerging at temperatures in excess of 300 °C, come into contact with cold seawater, precipitation of particles of metal oxides and sulphides makes them appear like clouds of black smoke (Figure 61) — hence the name **black smokers**.

Figure 61 Submarine hydrothermal activity — a black smoker chimney.

Several questions arise. — How do these black smokers form? Where do the fluids that emerge from black smokers come from? Why are they so hot? It is conceivable that hot watery fluid could separate from rising magma in the way that porphyry deposits are formed (Section 2.4). This could explain both their metal content and their heat, but at mid-ocean ridge sites, basaltic magma forms by melting of mantle rocks under dry conditions, and so contains very little water.

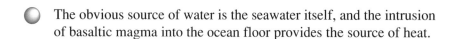

What other source of water would be available, and how could it be heated?

The obvious source of water is the seawater itself, and the intrusion of basaltic magma into the ocean floor provides the source of heat.

In volcanically active regions of the ocean floor, seawater penetrates cracks and fissures in piles of basaltic lava also made permeable by fragmentation and alteration, which occurred when it erupted into seawater. Within these hot volcanic rocks of the ocean floor, the seawater is heated to become a highly reactive saline fluid, which can alter minerals and leach metals (Block 1, Section 3.6.4). Convection returns these hot fluids to the ocean floor, rich in metals, such as iron, manganese, copper and zinc, which have been scavenged from the basaltic crust (Figure 62).

On emerging from the ocean floor, these hot fluids mix with cool seawater, and precipitate particles of sulphide and the more insoluble sulphate minerals to form a 'smoker'. Around the smoker vent, the accumulation of insoluble minerals — mainly anhydrite ($CaSO_4$), barite ($BaSO_4$) and metal sulphides — typically forms a cylindrical chimney-like deposit, as shown schematically in Figure 63. On the ocean floor, fluids emerge from the fractures that provide pathways to the surface. They form a mineralized stockwork, beneath mounds rich in sulphide minerals built up from the accumulation of collapsed chimneys. Eventually the escaping fluids deposit further sulphides

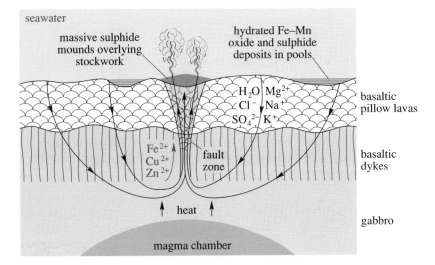

Figure 62 Convective circulation of hydrothermal fluids above 'hot spots' caused by igneous activity beneath the ocean floor. The initial salinity of the seawater enhances its reactivity to alter hot basalts and release metals into the fluid for its return to the ocean floor.

within the mounds to form **massive sulphide deposits**. Such mounds often extend 50 m across, more rarely up to hundreds of metres; they reach tens of metres in thickness, and contain a few million tonnes of sulphide minerals. Remains of similar ancient hydrothermal vents have been found in the ancient massive sulphide deposits of Cyprus and elsewhere.

A surprising feature of black smokers is that colonies of organisms live in and around the chimneys from which the hot hydrothermal brines emerge. The highly toxic complement of metals in these fluids might be expected to be one of the most unhealthy chemical cocktails imaginable, but some forms of organism actually thrive in these conditions, and, indeed, are found nowhere else. Some of these species may be related to some of the earliest forms of life to appear on Earth, and so black smokers are regarded by some as possible 'crucibles of life'.

Figure 63 The development of black smoker chimneys, sulphide mounds and mineralized stockwork, where hydrothermal fluids emerge from the ocean floor; the sulphide mounds are often fifty metres or more across.

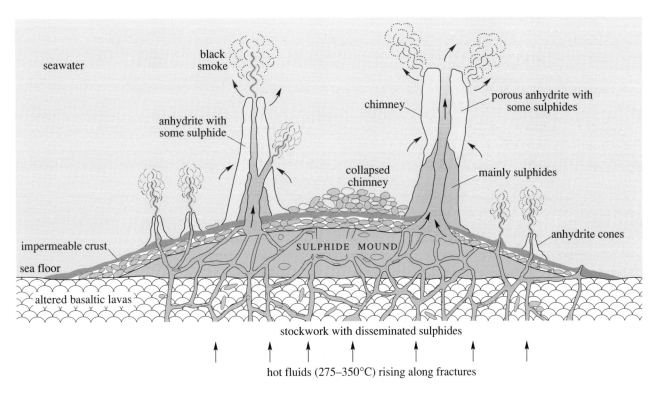

Red Sea hot brine pools and metalliferous muds

The Red Sea is a rather special feature of the Earth's surface. Bordered by continental crust that was joined 30 million years ago, it is floored by basaltic rock, new oceanic crust that is being formed along its axial zone, which is often described as a *rift valley*. It is probably the best example of continental break-up and the birth of a new ocean that is happening today.

Along the axial rift valley of the Red Sea, there are many hydrothermal features typical of oceanic spreading ridges, such as black smokers and basins containing hot brine pools, many of which also contain metalliferous sediments (Figure 64a). One such basin is the Atlantis II Deep, 14 km × 5 km in area, which contains over 200 Mt of metalliferous sediment, rich in manganese and iron oxides, and sulphides of iron, copper and zinc. Of this, 90 Mt, grading 2% Zn, 0.45% Cu and 38 g t^{-1} Ag, has formed during the last 15 000 years.

Is this deposit a renewable resource and good news for the sustainability of metals? Not really, because it amounts to only 6 000 t y^{-1}, of which just 120 t is

zinc — somewhat short of the 7.5 Mt of zinc metal that we *consume* globally each year!

Many of these basin deeps contain brines (as shown in Figure 64b), rather like hydrothermal solutions in terms of their salinity, reaching concentrations of 30% NaCl, and temperatures as high as to 60 °C. It is believed that salts are leached by seawater percolating through evaporites on the flanks of the Red Sea to give high-salinity solutions. These solutions pass through hot basalts below, from which they leach metals at temperatures above 250 °C, and are convected to discharge into the basin deeps. Although hot, their high density and the lack of large-scale circulation in the basins, causes the brines to be trapped, pooling beneath cool seawater (Figure 64b). On entering a brine pool, precipitation of metals occurs when the hot fluids cool, to form soft, muddy metalliferous sediments. Sulphide and sulphate minerals precipitate in the lower brines, and Fe–Mn oxides in the upper brines.

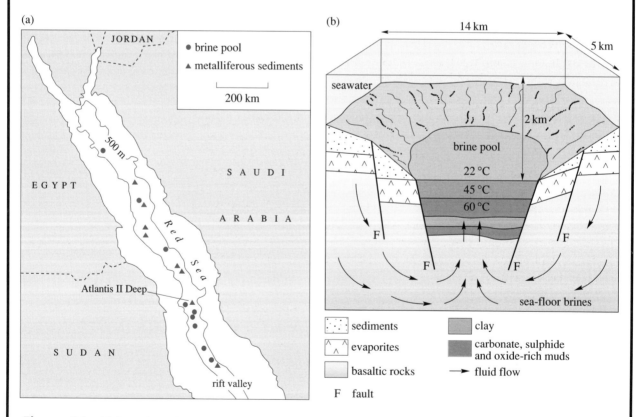

Figure 64 (a) Location of hot brine pools along the Red Sea rift valley. (b) A section across a brine pool in the Atlantis II Deep, showing temperature/density stratification of the brines and layers of metalliferous sediments. Although the brines are hot, they form pools because they are denser than the surrounding seawater owing to their high content of dissolved salts.

Mineral deposits being formed in association with black smokers at the present day are not confined to massive sulphide mounds, veined stockworks or encrusted chimneys (Figure 63). The sulphide-rich black smoke also disperses particles of oxide and sulphide minerals which accumulate in depressions of the ocean floor (Figure 62). If these *metalliferous* sediments are buried by layers of sediments or lavas, they can be preserved to form ore deposits. Sulphide layers from a deposit formed in this way, at Parys Mountain, Anglesey, are shown in Plate 69. Submarine, hydrothermally sourced deposits of this kind are not confined to sea-floor spreading centres, though the basins of the Red Sea (see box 'Red Sea hot brine pools and metalliferous muds') provide a classic example where metalliferous sediments are accumulating today. In the geological record, exhalative sulphide deposits are also known from sedimentary sequences where volcanic activity is *absent*. These include lead–zinc deposits in Ireland, which contain fossil hydrothermal vents similar to those described above.

It has long been recognized that massive sulphide deposits are found in sequences of volcanic rocks. One type, known as the Cyprus type (see box 'Massive sulphide deposits of Cyprus'), was once of great importance, but is now insignificant on the world scene. They are associated with basaltic volcanic rocks, and were originally formed on ocean floors at constructive plate boundaries. Although they are not very large individually, being at most a few hundred metres across and tens of metres thick, containing only a few million tonnes of reserves, they are widely spread across the world and are particularly rich in copper and zinc sulphides, chalcopyrite and sphalerite, which together form 5–15% of the deposit. The remainder of these deposits — indeed, the dominant part — is iron sulphide, largely in the form of pyrite (FeS_2). A network of mineralized veins, or stockwork, generally occurs beneath massive sulphide deposits, representing the pathways through which hydrothermal fluids emerged from the sea floor and providing additional sites for deposition of ore minerals (as featured in Figure 63).

Another form of massive sulphide deposit, known as Kuroko type, is named after deposits in Japan, of which there are over a hundred occurrences in eight districts along a zone extending for some 800 km. They are often associated with rhyolitic volcanic rocks of subduction-related volcanic arcs. They are usually larger than the Cyprus-type deposits, especially the examples of Precambrian age, such as the Golden Grove deposit in Western Australia and the Kidd Creek deposit of Canada (see box 'Kidd Creek massive sulphides — Kuroko type'). They formed in a similar way, but, because the crust that forms volcanic arcs, even oceanic ones, is different from oceanic crust, there are differences in source rock compositions, and the depth of water at which fluids are expelled is much shallower.

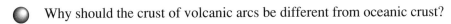 Why should the crust of volcanic arcs be different from oceanic crust?

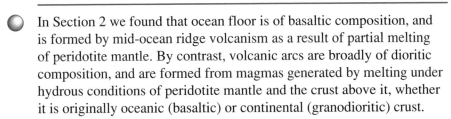 In Section 2 we found that ocean floor is of basaltic composition, and is formed by mid-ocean ridge volcanism as a result of partial melting of peridotite mantle. By contrast, volcanic arcs are broadly of dioritic composition, and are formed from magmas generated by melting under hydrous conditions of peridotite mantle and the crust above it, whether it is originally oceanic (basaltic) or continental (granodioritic) crust.

The crust of volcanic arcs is compositionally more variable than ocean floor crust, and contains higher levels of incompatible elements. Consequently, the elements concentrated in Kuroko-type deposits are more varied than in Cyprus-type deposits. They include lead, silver and gold, as well as copper and zinc, and there are also often large quantities of barite, gypsum and pyrite.

Massive sulphide deposits of Cyprus

The copper-rich massive sulphide deposits of Cyprus were mined by most of the ancient civilizations of the Mediterranean and the Middle East, including the Phoenicians, Greeks and Romans. Roman mining activity ended in the fourth century AD, and the mines were not re-opened until the late nineteenth century. Today, mining continues only on a very small scale.

There are about twenty massive sulphide deposits in Cyprus, all situated in the foothills of the Troodos Mountains, which form the southern half of the island (Figure 65a). These mountains represent a layered sequence of igneous rocks, comprising massive peridotite (mantle) at their core, passing upwards and outwards through layered peridotites (cumulates) and gabbros (basaltic intrusions) to a layer of mainly vertical 'sheeted' dykes (feeders) to pillow lavas (submarine extruded basalts) at the top of the sequence (Figure 65a). This rock sequence has led geologists to conclude that the Troodos mountains are made of *ophiolites* (Block 1, Section 3.6.4), rocks of the oceanic crust and upper mantle that have been lifted above sea-level by mountain-building processes.

The massive sulphide deposits are all located within the pillow lava sequences. Figure 65b shows a section through a typical deposit, which contained more than a million tonnes of ore with an average grade of 1.5% Cu, of which at least half was extracted in ancient times. The massive ore is composed mainly of pyrite (FeS_2), together with a small amount of quartz, chalcopyrite ($CuFeS_2$), a tiny proportion of sphalerite (ZnS) and other sulphides. Underlying the massive ore is a stockwork deposit in which sulphide minerals occupy veinlets and pockets between lava 'pillows' in a matrix of highly altered lava. The proportion of sulphides decreases downwards, so only the top of the stockwork was mined. Where the ore body is exposed at the surface, it has weathered to leave a leached but reddened capping of gossan. The layer beneath the capping is a secondary enrichment of chalcocite (Cu_2S), which was largely worked out by the miners of the ancient civilizations.

The total quantity of ore in all the Cyprus deposits, including that mined in ancient times, was probably around 50 million tonnes containing, on average, 2% Cu, 0.3% Zn and small amounts of gold and silver. The most profitable period in recent times was between 1925 and 1935, when unusually, pyrite was mined for both its iron and its sulphur (for use in the manufacture of sulphuric acid). In perspective, the total amount of copper produced from the Cyprus deposits in almost 5 000 years has been about 1 million tonnes, whereas the production of copper in the United States alone in 1992 was about 1.8 million tonnes, and that was less than a quarter of the world total in that year (Figure 36).

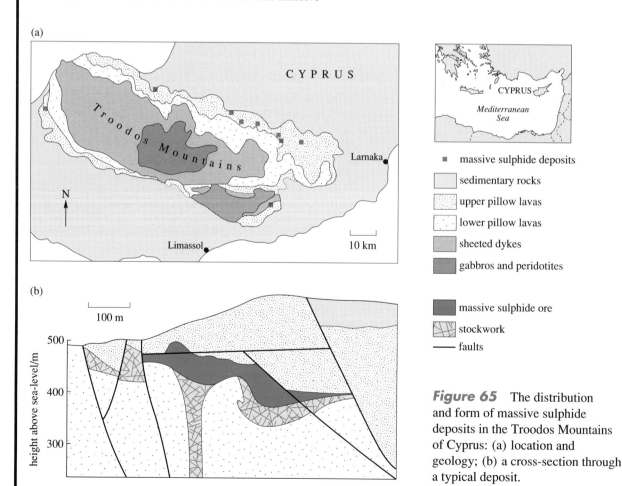

(a)

(b)

massive sulphide deposits

sedimentary rocks

upper pillow lavas

lower pillow lavas

sheeted dykes

gabbros and peridotites

massive sulphide ore

stockwork

faults

Figure 65 The distribution and form of massive sulphide deposits in the Troodos Mountains of Cyprus: (a) location and geology; (b) a cross-section through a typical deposit.

Kidd Creek massive sulphides—Kuroko type

The Kidd Creek Kuroko-type massive sulphide deposit of Ontario, Canada, occurs in ancient (2 700 Ma old) Precambrian volcanic rocks of the Canadian Shield. The ore body was not discovered until 1959. It had been hidden from old prospectors, who sought gold in the area, by boggy ground known as muskeg, and thick layers of glacial till. It was found by modern geophysical exploration techniques. Trial drilling proved over 8% Zn, 1.2% Cu and over 100 g t^{-1} Ag. The ore body turned out to be over 600 m long, up to 150 m wide, and to extend to a depth of at least 1 500 m (Figure 66).

● What do these dimensions tell us about the shape and orientation of the ore body? Bear in mind that massive sulphide mounds normally form on the sea floor as layers much thinner than they are wide.

○ The Kidd Creek ore body has been upended by Earth movements and is now orientated vertically rather than horizontally as it was formed.

Because of this form (Figure 66b), initial mining at Kidd Creek was as an open pit. Underground mining started in the 1970s and the open pit was abandoned in 1979.

From 1966 to 1989, 85 Mt of ore were mined, grading 7.2% Zn, 2.2% Cu, 0.28% Pb and 102 g t^{-1} Ag. At the beginning of 1990, reserves were estimated at 45 Mt, grading 5.1% Zn, 3.5% Cu, 0.16% Pb and 67 g t^{-1} Ag.

● How much copper is likely to be extracted in total from Kidd Creek, and how does this compare with all the copper mined on Cyprus?

○ $(85 \times 0.022) + (45 \times 0.035) = 3.4$ Mt copper. This compares with about 1 Mt copper in total from some twenty mine sites in Cyprus.

More copper was mined in a quarter of a century from the Kidd Creek deposit than was mined in several thousand years from many individual deposits in Cyprus. It is true that the Kidd Creek deposit is a particularly large example of a Kuroko-type massive sulphide deposit, but Kuroko-type deposits are, in general, larger than Cyprus-type massive sulphide deposits.

The massive ore at Kidd Creek contains pyrite, sphalerite, chalcopyrite and galena. Alongside it is a stockwork deposit of mainly chalcopyrite in fragmental rhyolite. This would have been the feeder zone for hydrothermal fluids beneath the massive sulphide deposit. Although the Kidd Creek deposit is Precambrian in age, the association of basalts (submarine pillow lavas), andesitic and rhyolitic lavas (Figure 66a) suggest a volcanic arc setting. The ore mineral assemblage is typical of Kuroko deposits.

Figure 66 The form of the Kidd Creek massive sulphide deposit, (a) in plan and (b) in cross-section.

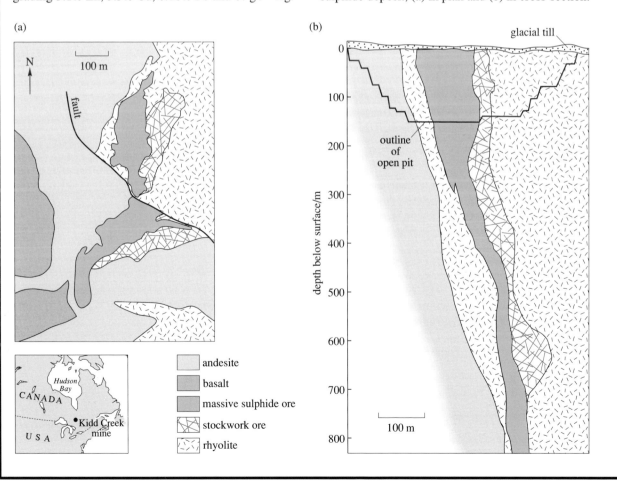

Case studies of Cyprus deposits and the Kuroko-type deposits of Kidd Creek demonstrate several contrasting features between these types of massive sulphide deposit. You have already come across one deposit that may be likened to Kuroko-type deposits — the site of the Parys Mountain copper mine in Anglesey, the subject of Video Band 2: *Copper — Resources and Reserves* and the location of the sulphide mineralization shown in Plate 69. It is also associated with rhyolitic volcanic rocks. Evaluation of the Parys Mountain deposit in the 1980s revealed 4.8 Mt ore, grading 3% Pb, 6% Zn, 1.5% Cu, 6.9 g t^{-1}Ag and 0.4 g t^{-1} Au. It has the potential to be the largest base metal mine in the UK with a planned output of 250 000 t y^{-1}, but because of depressed metal prices in the 1990s, the mine has not been developed.

Question 32

Summarize the formation of the ore deposits of Cyprus by completing the following table, recognizing how their formation may be explained in terms of SPADE.

Aspects of SPADE	Applicability to the ore deposits of Cyprus
Source: of ore constituents	
Pathways: for fluid circulation	
Agent: water supply	
Deposition: causes	
Deposition: site	
Energy: heat source	

4.3 Sub-surface hydrothermal ore deposits

We now consider the formation of ore deposits by hydrothermal systems at deeper levels within the crust. Clearly, there is some overlap between these systems and those of Section 4.2, where we were concerned with the deposition of ore minerals at and near to the surface; conceivably, they could be different parts of the same hydrothermal system. Here we are more concerned with *deposition in confined spaces* such as fractures to form veins (Figure 53a), and larger cavities to form massive ore bodies (Figure 53c). Such deposits are often associated with thick sequences of sedimentary rocks, which provide a source of fluids as groundwater and formation water, a source of scavengable metals in shales, and sites to deposit ore minerals in fracture zones or in permeable and soluble rocks such as limestones. These ore deposits can be divided according to the form of their heat source, into those associated with thick piles of sediment experiencing normal geothermal conditions (Section 4.3.1), and those associated with the emplacement of large igneous bodies, which not only provide a localized heat source but can supply magmatic fluids from the crystallizing magma (Section 4.3.2).

4.3.1 Hydrothermal ore deposits of sedimentary basins

World wide, much of the lead and zinc ore mined in recent years has come from deposits occurring in limestone rocks. These deposits contain the minerals galena (PbS), sphalerite (ZnS), barite (BaSO$_4$) and fluorite (CaF$_2$);

iron and copper sulphides are of minimal significance. According to evidence from fluid inclusions, they were deposits formed at temperatures of 50–180 °C. Clearly, the limestones themselves, composed mainly of calcium carbonate, are unlikely to have been sources of these metals. However, it is common for mineralized limestones to pass laterally into evaporites and shales, sedimentary formations that could provide both high-salinity fluids and sources of metals, as we shall see shortly.

In what geological setting might limestones, evaporites and shales be deposited in close proximity? Limestones usually form in shallow tropical waters, where accumulation of shelly material and/or growth of coral reefs is rapid and the supply of sediment from land is minimal. Shales are deposited as muds and silts in low-energy conditions, usually in deeper water. Of particular note are black shales, which contain organic matter that accumulates in reducing conditions and concentrates many trace metals (Section 3.3.1). Evaporites form along tropical coastlines as mud-flats or in lagoons where seawater has access and intermittent drying out occurs. An ideal setting in which all these rocks could form would be a tropical coastline with mud-flats or lagoons, and near-shore shallows, separated from a subsiding basin by an offshore reef. The setting of the Great Barrier Reef of Australia is a modern-day analogy.

Similar circumstances are shown in Figure 67, where a thick sequence of shales has accumulated in a subsiding sedimentary basin and limestones were formed in more gradually subsiding areas of shallow water. Increasing burial pressure compacts the pile of shales, driving out formation water potentially rich in metals. As the pile thickens, formation water is heated and convection combines with compaction to promote migration of hydrothermal fluids through permeable rock formations such as sandstones and limestones. Shale sequences are often much thicker than equivalent limestones, not only because shales are often deposited in the deeper waters of subsiding basins, but because shallow-water limestones are often intermittently uplifted and eroded.

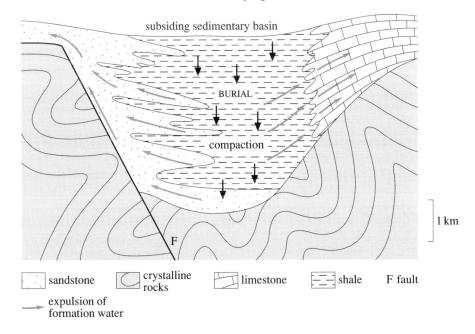

Figure 67 Burial of sediments in a sedimentary basin brings about heating and compaction of shales, and the expulsion of formation water into permeable sandstones and limestones.

 What is the likely effect on limestone of exposure to rainwater?

 Rainwater is acidic, so groundwater derived from it dissolves limestone along joints and fractures, and creates a network of solution channels and caverns, making suitable pathways for fluids and sites for ore mineral deposition from metal-bearing solutions.

Formation water from the shales and meteoric water that has percolated through evaporites may be very saline, and it, too, may be reactive as it penetrates permeable limestones. Metals, sulphur from the shales, and possibly even hydrocarbons may be carried as soluble complexes (Section 4.1.2) by shale-derived hydrothermal solutions. On entering the limestone environment, reaction between invading solutions, especially acidic ones, and the rock is likely to change the chemistry of the solution, and cause precipitation of ore minerals. The brines formed when groundwater percolates through evaporites may be another source of metals and sulphur as SO_4^{2-}, and may mix with shale-derived solutions to precipitate ore minerals within the limestone.

Similar circumstances and mechanisms of Pb–Zn ore formation are described for Pine Point in Canada in Video Bands 15 and 16. Pb–Zn deposits are also well known from locations in the UK, as featured in the box 'Lead–zinc orefields of Northern England'.

Now would be a good time to watch Video Band 15: *Pine Point: a lead–zinc deposit* and the first half of Video Band 16: *Pine Point: origin and exploration*. Although the programmes were made in the early 1980s, and mining ceased at Pine Point in 1987, their content is still just as relevant today, and they will help your wider appreciation of hydrothermal ore deposit formations. After watching, test your understanding of some of the more important points by answering the following Questions (33 to 36). It will probably help you to read these through quickly and have them fresh in your mind before viewing the videos. The questions and answers together will serve as a summary of the programme.

Video Band 15: Pine Point: a lead–zinc deposit
Video Band 16: Pine Point: origin and exploration

Speakers

John Wright	The Open University
Steve Drury	The Open University
Doug Shearman	Imperial College, London

The limestone-hosted lead–zinc deposits at Pine Point near the Great Slave Lake in the Northwest Territories of Canada are the subject of Video Bands 15 and 16. The location of the area and the geological setting of the deposits are illustrated in Figure 68.

Some 40 deposits were found in the area as isolated pockets, with a total reserve of 65 Mt of ore. Video Band 15 and the first half of Video Band 16 are about the occurrence and formation of the deposit. The remaining half of Video Band 16 and the whole of Video Band 17: *Pine Point: ore to metals*, need not be viewed now, because they describe methods of exploration and extraction — topics that will be discussed in *Metals 2*.

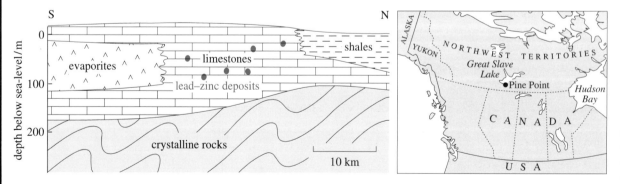

Figure 68 The geological setting of the Pine Point deposits. This schematic cross-section shows lead–zinc ore deposits as pockets (in colour) located in an ancient barrier reef limestone. Evaporites were formed behind the reef to the south and shales deposited on the seaward side to the north.

Question 33

(a) What were the main ore minerals at Pine Point?

(b) What were the ore grades for lead and zinc?

(c) How were the Pine Point deposits originally discovered?

Question 34

(a) What is meant by 'preparing the ground' for mineralization?

(b) What two processes provided the space for mineralization to occur?

(c) What factors influenced the shape of the Pine Point ore bodies, leading to working pits that are (i) circular and (ii) irregular in plan view?

Question 35

One of the following items (a) to (f) is *incorrect* in one simple respect. Which is it, and why is it wrong?

(a) In Devonian times, the limestone reef in which the Pine Point ore bodies are now found was a barrier between open sea to the north, where shales were deposited, and an extensive shallow basin to the south, where evaporites were formed.

(b) Associated with the lead–zinc ore minerals at Pine Point are natural bitumen (residual hydrocarbon), native sulphur and pyrite, all of which may be regarded as gangue minerals here.

(c) A fall in sea-level exposed the upper part of the limestone reef to weathering and erosion, allowing acidic groundwater to dissolve away parts of the limestone and form a complex network of caves and smaller cavities.

(d) Information about likely ore-forming reactions is provided by present-day surface waters and groundwaters in the Pine Point region. These contain both metal and sulphate ions in solution. Other spring waters contain dissolved hydrogen sulphide, and any lead or zinc ions coming into contact with them would cause the immediate precipitation of sulphide minerals.

(e) Compared with other factors, the remoteness of Pine Point had little influence on the time lag between systematic drilling in 1948, which proved the extent of the ore, and the first shipment of ore in 1965.

(f) The Pine Point ore bodies generally contain between 0.5 and 2 million tonnes of ore.

Question 36

In this question, attempt to use 'SPADE' as a framework for understanding the formation of the Pine Point ore deposit. Write a few sentences to answer each of the following.

Sources   Where might the metallic elements and the sulphur in the main ore minerals have come from?

Pathways   How did the ore minerals get into the limestone?

Agents   What was the nature of the agent that transported the ore mineral constituents and deposited the ore minerals? In what form were the ore mineral constituents transported?

Deposition   How were suitable sites for deposition prepared? What probably caused the precipitation of the ore minerals?

Energy   How might the mineralizing system have been driven?

Lead–zinc orefields of Northern England

The lead–zinc deposits of the North Pennines and Derbyshire occur in limestone. They were worked, until the mid-twentieth century, mainly for lead. Figure 69a shows that Carboniferous sediments in the North Pennines were deposited across relatively stable fault-bounded blocks (the Alston and Askrigg Blocks), mainly as limestones, and a more rapidly subsiding intervening basin (the Stainmore Trough), mainly as shales. Fluids containing 10–25% of dissolved salts were driven out of the compacting shales into the limestone, where galena and sphalerite were deposited as veins along faults and sedimentary discontinuities.

The main ore deposits are centred on the fault-bounded Alston and Askrigg Blocks as shown in Figure 69b. Alongside them, the worthless gangue, especially the minerals quartz, calcite, barite and fluorite also had to be extracted. In more recent times, some of these minerals have become more valuable than the ore minerals, and are mined as industrial minerals — barite for use as a drilling mud (Block 4 Part 1), and fluorite as a flux in the steel industry (Block 1, Section 1.3).

The mineralization of the Alston Block was at a slightly higher temperature (110–220 °C) than that of the Askrigg Block (90–165 °C). This may be explained by the presence of a very large granite body, the Weardale Granite, eroded even before Carboniferous sediment-ation occurred, which underlies the block, and may have contributed both to radioactive heating and the focusing of heat flow to a greater extent than the granite underlying the Askrigg Block (Figure 69a). The lead–zinc deposits of the Pennines, however, are not developed on such a large scale or in quite the same geological circumstances as some Irish and North American examples.

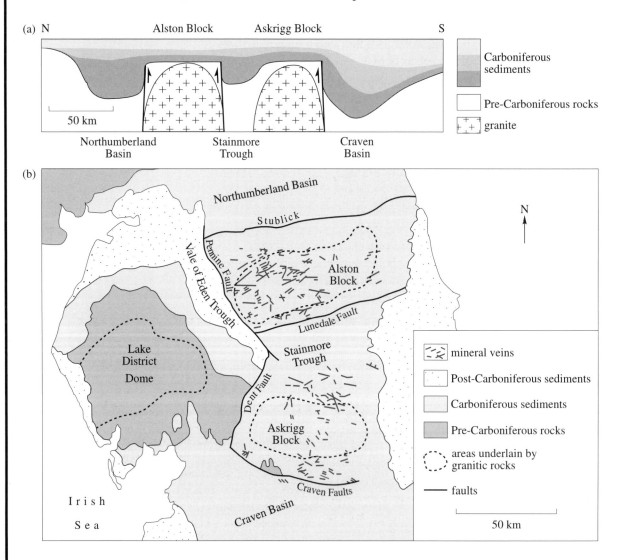

Figure 69 (a) North–south structure of the North Pennines after deposition of Carboniferous sediments; sediments were thickest in basins and thinnest overlying structural blocks, which subsided less, being underlain by granitic intrusions; (b) simplified geological map of northern England, showing the distribution of mineralized veins in the North Pennine orefield.

4.3.2 Hydrothermal ore deposits associated with large igneous intrusions

In a sedimentary basin, burial causes compaction and heating up of the sediment pile, leading to the expulsion of heated formation water (Figure 67). In these circumstances the energy input is gradual, depending on slow conduction of heat into the sediments during burial and their own internal radioactive heating. A more efficient means of heating that can take effect on a far shorter time-scale occurs when a large body of hot igneous rock is intruded. The heat associated with magma intrusion into sedimentary rocks provides energy to convect groundwater and may release water by dehydration of hydrous minerals. Accompanying tectonic activity opens fractures and joints, and facilitates the movement of water through what might otherwise be impermeable rock —including sedimentary and igneous rocks, and even crystalline parts of the intrusion itself.

○ How does this source reservoir in which fluids can access metals compare with the shale–limestone association encountered with lead–zinc deposits (Section 4.3.1), and what is the implication for the metals available for mineralization?

○ It contains a much broader spectrum of rock types including igneous rocks, which are capable of supplying a wider range of metals than encountered in limestone-related deposits.

A good example of this form of mineralization is associated with the large granite intrusions of Devon and Cornwall (see *The Geological Map* booklet, p. 24), an area probably best known for its tin deposits (see box 'Tin mineralization in Cornwall'). Granitic plutons are the most common large igneous bodies to be intruded into thick sedimentary sequences, and we know from our knowledge of pegmatite and porphyry ore deposits that they may themselves be a source of magmatic water and metals. Whereas the sediments they intrude may be sources of copper, zinc, lead, arsenic and sulphur, the granite may supply significant amounts of tin, tungsten and lithium. Although the hydrothermal fluids may be sourced largely from the surrounding sediments, some input, especially in the early stages, may come from fluids that separate from the crystallizing magma (as described in Section 2.1.2).

Tin mineralization in Cornwall

There is evidence to suggest that tin mining in Cornwall may date back some 5 000 years. Popular belief that the Phoenicians came to mine tin there has not been substantiated, but the Roman invasion of Britain may have been motivated in part by the knowledge of tin deposits. The Romans used tin to make bronze weapons, tools and coins. Most of the early mining was from alluvial deposits; it was easier to recover cassiterite from sands and gravels than from rock exposures. Only in the fifteenth century did underground working start to become more important. The mining was highly labour intensive, and tunnels and shafts were cut by hand until the late seventeenth century, when gunpowder became available for blasting and engines for pumping water. The scale of mining increased with progressive industrialization in the seventeenth and eighteenth centuries, reaching a peak at the middle of the nineteenth century, when copper, lead and arsenic were also mined.

It has been estimated that, in all, about 2.5 Mt of tin and almost 2 Mt of copper have been extracted from the area. There were about 2 500 mining operations, but most had closed by the end of the nineteenth century due to depletion of reserves and a collapse of tin prices as sources became available from abroad. Of the few mines that survived into the twentieth century, Geevor and South Crofty were probably the most successful. Rising tin prices in the 1960s encouraged several other mines such as Wheal Jane to re-open, but a crash in the tin price in 1985 led to more closures, and by 1995 only South Crofty survived —just.

Most of the tin occurs in quartz veins (known to miners as 'lodes') in which the main tin-bearing mineral is

---

cassiterite (SnO_2), occurring together with the minor minerals stannite (Cu_2FeSnS_4), wolframite ($FeWO_4$) and chalcopyrite ($CuFeS_2$). The main ore-bearing lodes occur around the edges and roofs of the granite bodies of Devon and Cornwall (shown in Figure 70a), which were emplaced 270–300 Ma ago. To the Cornish miners the rocks were basically of two types: the granites, and the rocks intruded by the granites, largely sedimentary and volcanic rocks, which they called 'killas'.

Cornwall has a particular interest for economic geologists because of the well-developed zonal distribution of the ore minerals around the granites, which is illustrated in Figure 70b. Nearest to the granite, minerals of tin and tungsten are most abundant, then comes a zone dominated by copper minerals, then a zone of lead and zinc minerals and, finally, a zone of iron minerals. Studies of fluid inclusions have shown that these zones correlate with decreasing temperature of the hydrothermal fluids: the tin–tungsten lodes were formed at temperatures of 300–400 °C, whereas the lead–zinc and iron lodes were formed at temperatures below 150 °C. Isotopic studies have shown that the hydrothermal fluids were derived mainly from the surrounding sediments, and set in convective motion by the hot granitic intrusions (Figure 70c). They were able to scavenge metals from the sediments (Cu, Zn, Pb and Fe), and from the consolidated granite (Sn and W) as well. Where access to the granite was possible through joints and fractures, the granitic wall rocks were extensively altered, providing an additional source of metals.

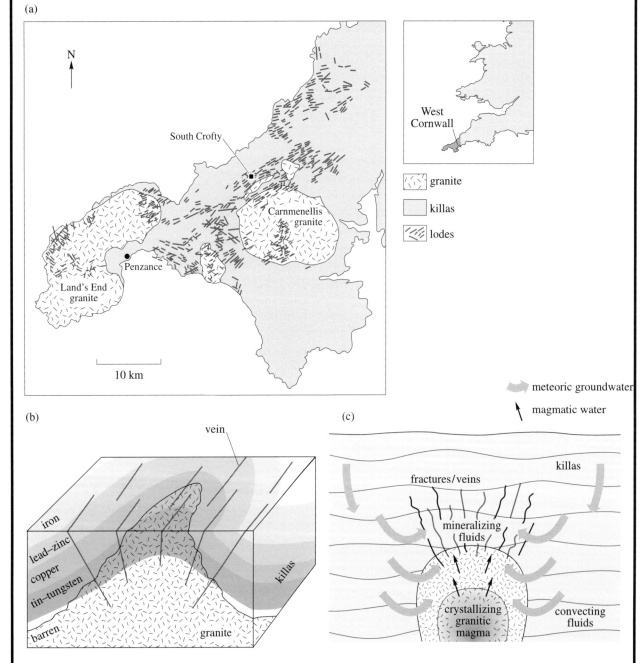

Figure 70 Mineralization in west Cornwall: (a) the distribution of mineralized hydrothermal vein deposits (lodes); (b) the zonation of ore minerals around the granitic intrusions; (c) the circulation and sources of mineralizing fluids.

Question 37

By completing Table 19, summarize similarities and differences in the circumstances by which the Pine Point and Cornish ore deposits were formed. Insert the items from the list below the Table, into their appropriate location.

Table 19 SPADE summary of the formation of the Pine Point and Cornish ore deposits

Location: metal ores	*Source* of ore constituents	Source of water *agent*	*Pathways* for fluid circulation	Cause of ore *deposition*	Site of ore *deposition*	Source of heat *energy*
Pine Point: Pb, Zn					cavities in limestone	
Cornwall: Sn, W, Cu, Zn, Pb					large fractures	

Items to choose from:

shales, evaporites

joints and fractures

normal geothermal heating

emplacement of granite

meteoric and formation water

sedimentary rocks, volcanic rocks, granite

joints, fractures and solution cavities

reaction with limestone and cooling

cooling and reaction with wall rocks

meteoric, formation and magmatic waters

4.4 Summary of Section 4

1 Hydrothermal systems involve the *movement* of large volumes of hot, aqueous fluids through pathways in the crust in response to:

(i) convection—driven by normal geothermal heating or igneous intrusion; and/or

(ii) compaction—through burial of wet sediments.

2 To form a hydrothermal ore deposit also requires:

(i) an extensive and fertile source of ore mineral constituents (metals and sulphur especially);

(ii) a fluid of suitable composition to extract and transport those constituents;

(iii) a suitable site where space is available for deposition, to which prolonged fluid flow is focused, and where local conditions favour the precipitation of ore minerals.

3   Compositions of hydrothermal fluids, and of the ores they may produce, depend on the source of the water and on the assemblage of source rocks that they leach. Therefore different types of deposit, in terms of their form and typical ore minerals, are associated with different geological environments. However, the *principles* that govern the concentration of metals — involving the leaching of large volumes of rock, the transportation of soluble components and the localized precipitation of ore minerals — are always the same.

4   Exhalative hydrothermal deposits can be seen forming on the Earth's surface at the present day, both on land (associated with hot springs) and on the ocean floor (associated with black smokers) in areas of active volcanism.

(a)   Hydrothermal systems associated with hot springs may form high-grade gold-bearing veins and breccias well below ground level, and low-grade disseminated gold in more extensive replacement and alteration zones.

(b)   Hydrothermal systems associated with sea-floor volcanism form submarine massive sulphide deposits, known as Cyprus-type, when formed in oceanic settings, and Kuroko-type, in volcanic arc settings.

5   Hydrothermal deposits formed within continental crust are often associated with thick sequences of sediments in which background geothermal heat may be enhanced by the intrusion of large igneous bodies. They commonly occur as vein deposits within fractured rocks.

(a)   Limestones sometimes host low-temperature hydrothermal lead–zinc deposits in veins and in solution cavities. Interaction of hydrothermal fluid either with limestone or another fluid may cause the deposition of ore minerals; both fluids and metals may be derived from associated shales and evaporites.

(b)   High-temperature hydrothermal tin–tungsten vein deposits are often associated with large granitic intrusions, which provide additional heat as well as metals and fluids; but most of the fluid and the metals for accompanying copper, lead and zinc mineralization are derived from surrounding, usually mainly sedimentary, rocks.

5 GLOBAL OCCURRENCE OF ORE DEPOSITS

This final Section aims to place the formation of ore deposits into the context of the rock cycle and their plate tectonic setting, and then examine their global distribution and age. It is important to appreciate how the form and occurrence of particular ore deposits are controlled by geological processes and relate to large-scale global settings before we start to explore the more practical aspects of metals exploitation in *Metals 2*.

First, let's make some general observations about the natural concentration processes that may produce ore deposits. These processes are all, in effect, mechanisms of *fractionation*, the selective separation of fractions or components in a system, which can occur by either physical or chemical means. Thus, we have encountered:

- magmatic fractionation, in which dense mineral and/or immiscible liquid fractions separate at high temperature in cooling magma to form *magmatic segregation deposits*. During crystallization and reduction of pressure on emplacement, wet magmas may release watery fluids and form *porphyry ore deposits*. Extreme concentration of incompatible elements and water in magma remaining after crystallization may form a mobile melt fraction and, ultimately, *pegmatite deposits*.

- sedimentary fractionation by *mechanical separation* of high-density grains from low-density and/or fine-grained materials to form heavy mineral-enriched *placer deposits*. This form of fractionation also gives rise to resources such as sands, gravels and clays as used for construction materials (Block 2).

- aqueous fractionation by *chemical separation* of substances with different solubilities in aqueous solution. Such processes operate in both surface and subsurface environments, and either remove soluble materials to leave insoluble fractions — forming *residual deposits* — or precipitate insoluble fractions to form *hydrothermal deposits* and *sedimentary precipitates*, leaving soluble material in solution, eventually to accumulate in the oceans and potentially to produce evaporite deposits.

Another form of fractionation involves the heating and 'distillation' of volatile organic materials during the formation of fossil fuels — forming concentrations of gas, oil and coal, as discussed in Block 4 Part 1.

5.1 Mineral deposits in the rock cycle

You were introduced to the rock cycle in Block 1 (Section 3.5.5) and have revisited it in various guises since, so the main principles should be familiar to you. In particular, Video Band 3: *Resource Geology* considered a number of physical resources — among them certain types of ore deposits — in the context of the rock cycle. Here we shall see how the various types of ore deposit encountered in this Block fit into this unifying scheme. Figure 71 provides a schematic framework in which all the ore deposits are shown in their geological setting. As this diagram is quite complex and will need some time to appreciate fully, it is the subject of Audio Band 6: *Ore Deposits and the Rock Cycle*, which relates the occurrence and formation of ore deposits to the geological processes of the rock cycle. However, it contains nothing new and should help you to consolidate your understanding of earlier Sections of this Block.

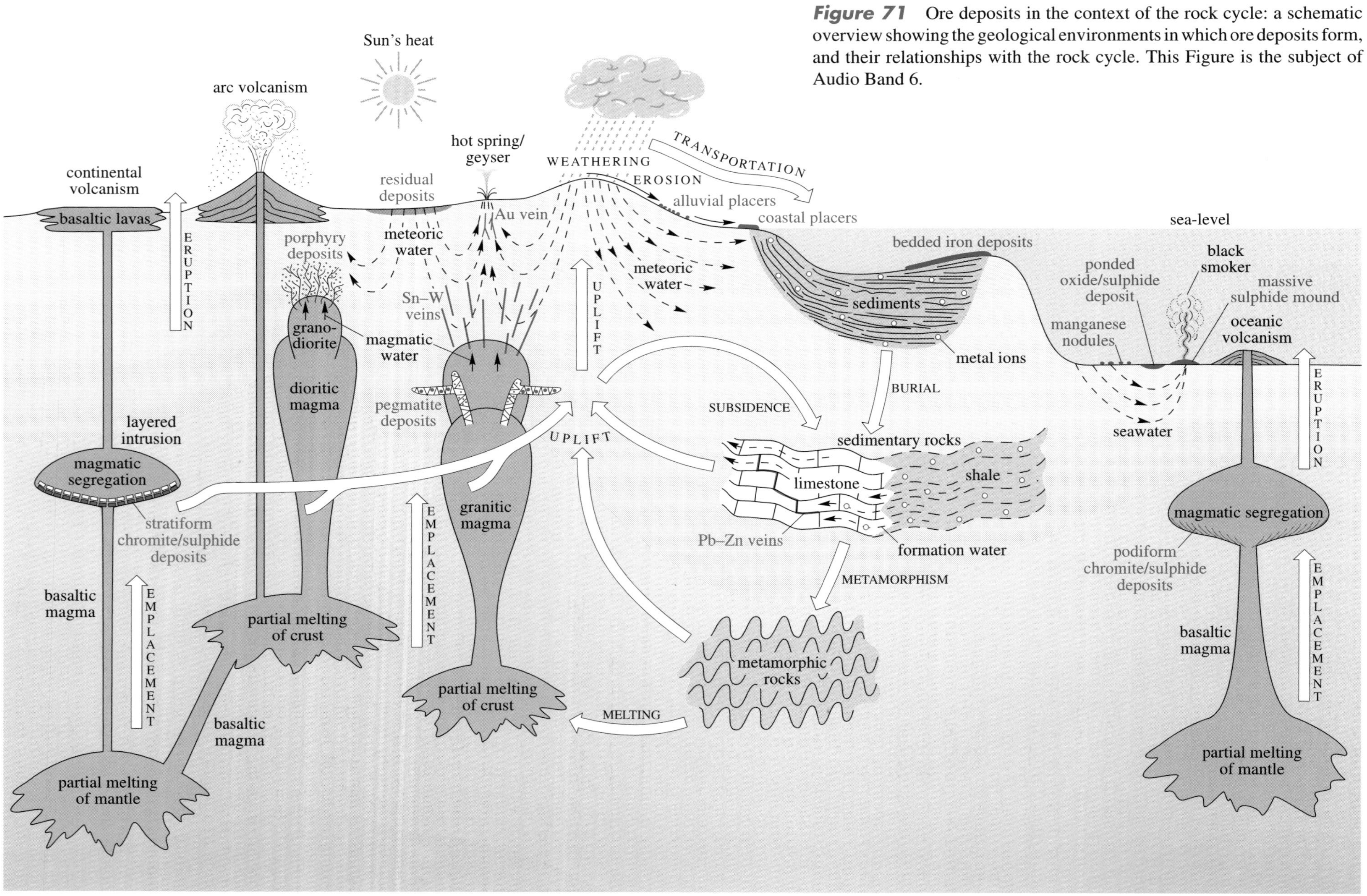

Figure 71 Ore deposits in the context of the rock cycle: a schematic overview showing the geological environments in which ore deposits form, and their relationships with the rock cycle. This Figure is the subject of Audio Band 6.

Figure 71 has many features that are reminiscent of the rock cycle shown in Block 1, Figure 60. The diagram includes the geological processes that provide linkages between the main rock types. These processes include:

- partial melting of hot mantle and crustal (metamorphic) rocks to form magmas;
- magma emplacement as intrusions into crust and its possible eruption at the Earth's surface to form volcanic rocks;
- erosion and weathering of surface rocks followed by transportation and deposition to form sediments;
- subsidence of crust and burial of sediments, followed by heating and metamorphism to form metamorphic rocks;
- uplift of crust by tectonic activity to bring all types of buried rock to the Earth's surface.

We have already noted that many of these processes may concentrate elements and are essentially the same as those that form mineral deposits. Only if concentration processes operate efficiently, for a long enough time, and on a large enough scale, however, can sufficient concentration occur to form an economically exploitable ore deposit.

The extreme right of Figure 71 covers deposits formed in oceanic environments. These do not fit simply into the rock cycle because oceanic crust is usually subducted and lost into the mantle. However, ocean-floor material is sometimes thrust onto continental crust and then enters the rock cycle.

Now listen to Audio Band 6 for a more detailed discussion of Figure 71. In addition to Figure 71, which sets the ore deposits discussed in this Block into a broad geological framework, you should also refer to Table 20, which summarizes their mode of formation and includes some typical examples from this Block.

Audio Band 6   Ore deposits and the rock cycle

Speaker

Peter Webb   The Open University

Geochemical cycles

A fascinating aspect of geochemistry in the context of the rock cycle is that Earth materials and their component elements travel around the rock cycle in lots of different ways. Just as water travels at different rates and by different routes through the water cycle, so do metals through the rock cycle. For example, detrital heavy mineral grains may be deposited in sediments at the coast, they may be buried, compacted and lithified, only to be uplifted and exposed to weathering once again, to release mineral grains for transportation once more to the coast. Alternatively, heavy mineral grains may accumulate within sediments of basins formed between closing continental masses and become buried to great depth during collision and crustal thickening, to be incorporated into molten rock. The resulting magma then enters the igneous part of the rock cycle, possibly to crystallize as intrusions or to erupt at the surface and form new heavy minerals. With uplift, weathering and erosion, detrital heavy mineral grains may be produced once again.

In different situations, the time-scale of geochemical cycling is likely to be very different. In general, near-surface cyclic activity occurs on the shortest time-scale. This could be as little as tens of thousands of years but is more likely to be hundreds of thousands of years. Cyclic activity at greater depth

Table 20 Summary of ore deposits described in this Block, their mode of formation and typical occurrences

Type	Mode of formation	Representative deposits
ORES FORMED by IGNEOUS PROCESSES (SECTION 2)		
magmatic segregation deposits (Section 2.2)	settling of dense, early-formed minerals to the floor of a magma chamber during consolidation	chromite, precious metal and magnetite layers of the Bushveld Complex, South Africa
	settling of dense immiscible sulphide or oxide melts to the floor of a magma chamber during consolidation	copper–nickel deposits of Sudbury, Ontario; titanium deposits of Allard Lake, Quebec
pegmatite deposits (Section 2.3)	separation and crystallization of remaining melt, rich in water and incompatible elements, during the final stages of consolidation of a granitic magma	uranium deposits at Rössing, Namibia; lithium deposits of Greenbushes, Australia, and Bernic Lake, Manitoba
porphyry ore deposits (Section 2.4)	separation of magmatic metal-rich aqueous fluids, leading to explosive fracturing on boiling and expulsion into tiny fractures in the surrounding rocks; overprinted by meteoric fluids	porphyry copper deposits of the South American Andes, at Chuquicamata, Chile; porphyry molybdenum deposits of Climax, Colorado
ORES FORMED by SURFACE PROCESSES (SECTION 3)		
residual and secondary enrichment deposits (Section 3.2)	intense weathering, leaching soluble salts, leaving concentrations of insoluble material near the surface; precipitation of ore minerals at deeper levels	bauxite ores of Jamaica, Guinea and Australia; nickeliferous laterites of New Caledonia; enriched porphyry copper deposits, Miami, Arizona
sedimentary precipitates (Section 3.3)	precipitation from solution or colloidal state to form bedded deposits in suitable sedimentary environments, mainly in shallow seas or in the deep oceans	banded iron formations of Lake Superior, North America and Hamersley Ranges, Australia; ironstones of Europe; manganese nodules of the ocean floor
placer deposits (Section 3.4)	sedimentary accumulation of heavy mineral grains in river and coastal environments	alluvial placer gold deposits of Australia and California; alluvial tin deposits of Malaysia; beach placer ilmenite and rutile deposits of Australia
ORES FORMED by HYDROTHERMAL PROCESSES (SECTION 4)		
surface and near-surface deposits (Section 4.2)	deposition of ore on and just beneath both the sea floor and land surfaces from hot aqueous solutions after circulation through the crust	gold-bearing hot spring-related deposits of Nevada; massive Cu–Zn sulphide deposits of Cyprus and Kidd Creek, Ontario; metal-rich sediments of the Red Sea
sub-surface deposits (Section 4.3)	deposition of ore within the crust after circulation of hot aqueous solutions through sedimentary rock formations and/or around igneous intrusions	base metal (Pb–Zn) deposits of the Pennines and North America (Pine Point); tin–tungsten deposits of Cornwall

involving major tectonic events is likely to require a much longer time-scale — a minimum of several tens of millions of years but more likely several hundreds of millions of years.

Additional information about the main types of ore deposit is given in Table 21, which is part of Activity 4. As part b of the Activity is to correct *deliberate mistakes*, you should *not accept its contents until you have completed the Activity*. It summarizes the main metals concentrated in each deposit, describes the agent involved, the main concentration processes and the environment of deposition. You should be aware, however, that it is not always easy to classify ore deposits into neat pigeon-holes. In real situations there are gradations and overlaps between many types of deposit, on account of similarities in the concentration processes involved in their formation. Many of the differences between deposits are due to the geological environments in which they occur and the compositions of accessible sources of metals.

Activity 4

This Activity concerns Table 21, and will be a useful revision exercise for you. It should help to reinforce some of the main points about the ore deposits that we have examined.

(a) Work out which of the following ten items relate to the headings: 'Geological environment', 'Concentration processes', 'Agent' or 'Typical metals'; then insert each into its correct place in Table 21.

Cu, Ag	roof zones of granitic intrusions
mainly meteoric water	formation, meteoric and magmatic waters
mainly seawater	layers in gabbroic intrusions
Cu, Mo (Sn)	residue left after weathering and removal of soluble ions
surface water	hydrothermal precipitation, mixing fluids, host rock reaction

(b) Find and *correct* the following four sets of deliberate mistakes in the Table:
  (i)   Geological environments for two types of deposit have been swapped.
  (ii) Concentration processes for two types of deposit have been swapped.
  (iii) Agents for two types of deposit have been swapped.
  (iv) Typical metals for two types of deposit have been swapped.

Table 21 Summary of ore deposit formation (for use with Activity 4, which involves correction of deliberate mistakes in this Table)

Deposit type	Geological environment	Concentration processes	Agent	Typical metals
magmatic segregation		density settling of mineral grains and blobs of melt	basaltic magma (sulphide/oxide melt)	Cr, Ni, Cu, PGEs, Ti
pegmatite		melt remaining after fractional crystallization	water-saturated granitic magma	Li, U, Ta, Cs, Be, Nb
porphyry	shallow porphyry intrusions in volcanic arcs	separation of aqueous fluid from magma, explosive fracturing, mixing with groundwater, reaction with host rocks and cooling	magmatic aqueous fluid (early); meteoric fluid (later)	
residual	rivers/coasts		seawater	Al, Fe, Ni, Co, Au
secondary enrichment	near-surface, mineralized deposits	leaching and deposition	meteoric groundwater	
bedded iron ore	submarine, shallow seas	sedimentary precipitation	meteoric surface water	Fe
manganese nodules	submarine, deep ocean	sedimentary sorting	seawater	(Mn, Fe, Ni, Co, Cu, Zn)*
placer	surface, tropical areas	sedimentary precipitation		Sn, Ti, Au
hot spring-related	near-surface, land-based, hydrothermally active regions	hydrothermal precipitation, cooling fluids		Pb, Zn
massive sulphide	submarine, hydrothermally active region	hydrothermal precipitation, cooling fluids		Cu, Zn, Pb
sedimentary basin	sedimentary pile with shales, limestones and evaporites		mainly formation and meteoric waters	Au, Ag, Hg
granite intrusion -related	granite intruded into sedimentary pile	hydrothermal precipitation, cooling fluids		Sn, W, Cu, Zn, Pb

* These metals do not form ore deposits of this kind at present.

5.2 Mineralization and plate tectonics: the global refinery

When the large-scale tectonic behaviour of the Earth was understood in terms of plate tectonics, it became possible to place the *main processes of the rock cycle* into a global context. The *generation of magmas* occurs at constructive plate margins to form new ocean floor, and at destructive plate margins to form volcanic arcs; *metamorphism and crustal melting* occurs in deformed and thickened crust after collision between continents and/or volcanic arcs and by intrusion of hot magmas. Both crustal collision events and intrusion of hot magmas into volcanic arcs may cause rapid *uplift*, which promotes *erosion* and subsequent *sedimentation*, and this in turn leads to the accumulation of thick piles of sediments. Thus, plate tectonics not only provides the setting in which the rock cycle operates, but the driving force for many of its processes.

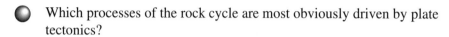 Which processes of the rock cycle are most obviously driven by plate tectonics?

○ Any process that involves movements of lithospheric plates or heating related to magmatism at plate boundaries is directly or indirectly driven by plate tectonics. Most forms of igneous activity relate to plate tectonics, especially at mid-ocean ridges and volcanic arcs; so too are major movements of the crust involving uplift and subsidence, especially when linked to continental collision.

5.2.1 Deposits formed at constructive plate margins

Beneath sea-floor spreading centres along mid-ocean ridges, where oceanic crust is continually being generated, basaltic magma is formed by partial melting of peridotite mantle and intruded into the crust along a narrow linear zone.

● What two important types of ore-forming *process* have we encountered that could occur at mid-ocean ridges?

○ (i) *Magmatic segregation* by crystal fractionation or liquid immiscibility on emplacement and cooling of hot, fluid basaltic magmas, to form ore deposits in magma chambers (Section 2.2).

(ii) *Leaching by and deposition from* hydrothermal solutions produced when emplacement of hot magma causes seawater within the ocean floor to heat up and circulate. The hot seawater leaches metals and may form ore deposits on emergence from the ocean floor (Section 4.2.2).

The main types of ore deposits formed by these processes are shown in Figure 72. They are:

(i) chromite deposits, which, when found in continental settings in ophiolite belts, occur as podiform deposits — frequently lens-shaped as a result of their tectonic emplacement;

(ii) Cyprus-type massive copper–zinc sulphide deposits, overlying stockwork mineralization and sometimes with relict 'black smoker' chimneys, and accumulated layers of sulphide- and oxide-rich sediments in basins.

However, mineral deposits of the ocean floor can only become ore deposits if they are accessible. Although both podiform chromite and Cyprus-type massive sulphide deposits were *formed* as part of the oceanic crust at constructive plate margins, they now *occur* in continental settings such as the Alpine–Himalayan mountain belt, a linear zone where continental masses came together in Tertiary times, squeezing out of existence an ancient ocean called Tethys.

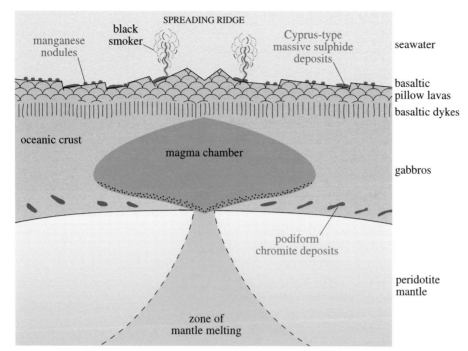

Figure 72 The occurence of podiform chromite and Cyprus-type massive sulphide deposits at a constructive plate margin.

⬤ How is it that deposits once formed at a constructive plate margin could be found today along a destructive plate margin, which might be thousands of kilometres from where they formed?

○ When plates come together at a destructive margin, especially during continental collision, fragments of oceanic crust may be thrust onto continental crust to form ophiolite complexes (Block 1, Section 3), thus providing access to mineral deposits originally formed on and within the ocean floor.

5.2.2 *Deposits formed at destructive plate margins*

During subduction of oceanic lithosphere (crust and mantle) at destructive plate margins, heating and dehydration of the hydrous minerals within the oceanic crust causes watery fluids to be driven off, to rise into the mantle overlying the descending slab (Figure 73). Consequent wet melting of the mantle forms wet magmas, which rise and interact with overlying crustal material to form a range of magma compositions usually dominated by dioritic magma.

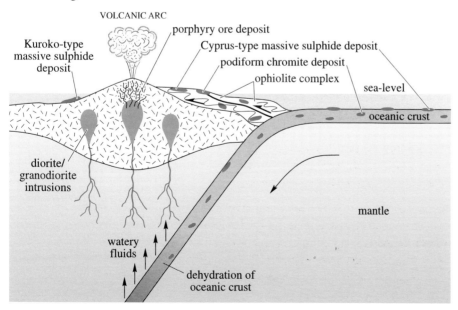

Figure 73 The occurrence of ore deposits in oceanic volcanic arcs at destructive plate margins.

137

● What ore-forming processes are associated with magmatism in volcanic arc settings?

● When wet magmas are emplaced at a high level in the crust, dissolved magmatic water may separate, even boil, and the explosive release of vapour can shatter the surrounding rocks. As metal-rich magmatic fluids escape, and mix with groundwaters, they may form disseminated, porphyry ore deposits.

Porphyry copper deposits are probably the best-known porphyry ore deposits, as they have become an increasingly important source of copper during the twentieth century. Molybdenum porphyries are now the main source of molybdenum. The global distribution of porphyry copper and molybdenum deposits shown in Figure 74 is closely linked to volcanic arcs, particularly the continental arcs of the Andes, the Sierran ranges of North America, and the oceanic arcs of the western Pacific. This restricted distribution associated with subduction zones and former subduction zones (Figure 74) is an important consideration when exploring for new copper and molybdenum deposits.

Where volcanic arcs are formed in a submarine environment, the combination of hot magmas and seawater is similar to that occurring at mid-ocean ridges (Section 5.2.1).

● What kind of hydrothermal ore deposits might we expect to form in submarine volcanic arcs?

● Exhalative massive sulphide deposits, rather like those at mid-ocean ridges.

Figure 74 The global distribution of porphyry copper and molybdenum deposits in relation to tectonic plate boundaries.

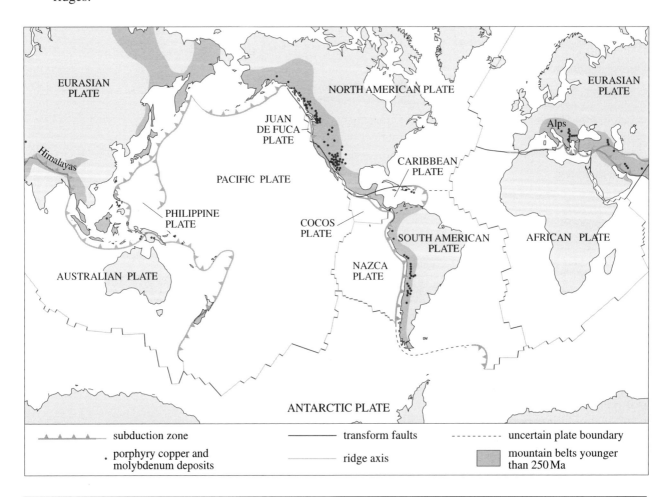

These are the Kuroko-type massive sulphide deposits described in Section 4.2.2. The compositions of subduction-related volcanic rocks and volcanic arc crust are more variable than those of the basalts and oceanic crust formed at mid-ocean ridges. As a result Kuroko-type massive sulphide deposits often contain silver, gold and lead as well as copper and zinc. In continental arcs, emplacement of magmas may lead to the formation of hydrothermal systems involving meteoric water, producing hot spring deposits at the surface and mineralization at shallow depth (Section 4.2.1), deposits that have been worked in recent years for disseminated gold.

5.2.3 Deposits formed as a result of collision events

Collision events occur at destructive plate margins. They involve continental masses or island arcs carried along with subducting lithosphere, and generally mark the end of an episode of subduction. Some of the deposits already reviewed (especially oceanic podiform chromites and Cyprus-type hydrothermal deposits) may be *preserved* as a result of collision, but here we are concerned with deposits that would not be *formed* without collision. Crustal thickening associated with collision arises either directly through folding and thrusting (low-angle compressive faulting), as shown in Figure 75, or, secondarily, by subsidence of adjacent areas where eroded material from rapidly uplifted land accumulates.

Abnormally thick crust may partially melt at depth and form granitic magmas, which may become enriched in incompatible elements during crystallization of late-stage melt fractions, and pegmatites may be formed (Figure 75). Emplacement of granitic magmas at shallow depth heats the crust to cause circulation of hydrothermal fluids, from which high-temperature hydrothermal vein deposits form (Figure 75). These deposits are most important for tin–tungsten mineralization (Section 4.3.2), and pegmatites for lithium, beryllium, tantalum and uranium mineralization (Section 2.3). The occurrence of these deposits is often related to ancient collision zones, where erosion has exposed the roofs of granitic intrusions.

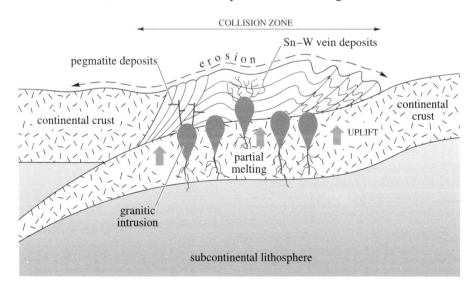

Figure 75 Occurrence of pegmatite and Sn–W vein deposits associated with granitic intrusions formed as a result of a continental collision event.

5.2.4 Deposits formed within tectonic plates

The main difference between the interiors of tectonic plates and plate margins is the relative stability of plate interiors, whereas deformation and tectonic instability are features of plate boundaries. Ore deposits formed in regions of stable crust include the Precambrian banded iron formations (BIF), where deposition is believed to have occurred over long periods of time within a stable tectonic regime. The largest magmatic deposits — the stratiform

ores such as those in the Bushveld Complex — were also formed in tectonically stable regimes, but at locations where there had been significant
melting of mantle beneath the continental crust. The distribution of the
most important iron deposits, the BIF, and stratiform magmatic segregation deposits are today confined to those areas of ancient crust more than
2 000 Ma old, known as *cratons* (Figure 76). Such very old continental
interiors have been involved in some tectonic activity, but have generally
been tectonically stable for long periods of time.

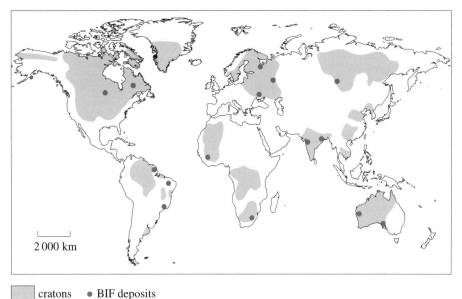

2 000 km

▨ cratons   • BIF deposits

Figure 76 Distribution of
Precambrian BIF deposits and
ancient stable cratons.

Question 38

When exploring for particular mineral deposits, it can be useful to know
whether to look in a *specific* plate tectonic setting. Some of the following types
of ore deposit are formed in a specific plate tectonic setting. Identify which
they are and specify the setting in which you would expect to find them:

(i)   porphyry copper deposits;

(ii)   secondary enrichment deposits;

(iii) placer deposits;

(iv)   massive sulphide deposits;

(v)   hot spring deposits;

(vi)   residual deposits.

5.3 The age and distribution of ore deposits

The workings of the rock cycle and of major tectonic processes through
geological time have created an irregular global distribution of ore deposits.
We have already come across some evidence of this variability, for example
in the concentration of platinum and chromium ores in the Bushveld region
of South Africa, and in the location of porphyry copper deposits in the
volcanic arcs around the Pacific Ocean. Our earlier discussions of ore
deposit formation tell us why the distribution is so irregular: it is essentially
because different kinds of ore deposit are produced in specific geological
circumstances; globally, these circumstances have arisen due to a range of
geological and tectonic processes, acting at different places and at different
times to form the Earth's crust in an irregular manner over geological time.

An important consequence of all this is that areas of similar geological development contain similar ore deposits. This principle is a valuable exploration guide for economic geologists. Geological characteristics of particular importance are age and tectonic setting.

Age dependence of ore deposits

Attempt the following question in order to familiarize yourself with the periods of geological time in which certain types of deposit tend to occur, and the likely explanation for the observations cited.

Question 39

Match the following series of *observations* with the *explanations* beneath. (*Hint* Take each observation in turn, and look for clues in the explanations.)

Observations

(a) The world's most extensive and richest deposits of iron ore occur in ancient rocks, 1 900–2 500 Ma old.

(b) The majority of lead–zinc deposits in limestones occur in rocks about 300–400 Ma old.

(c) Vein deposits of tin, and porphyry deposits of copper and molybdenum, are rarely very old; most are younger than 200 Ma, and very few are older than 400 Ma.

(d) Bauxite deposits are generally quite young; they are rarely older than 65 Ma.

(e) Placer deposits of uranium are older than 2 400 Ma.

Explanations for matching

(i) Deposits formed at the Earth's surface on land are likely to be dispersed and destroyed by weathering and erosion, especially when uplift occurs.

(ii) In Devonian and Carboniferous times, extensive development of shallow basins in tropical latitudes resulted in thick sequences of limestone being deposited along coasts. Limestone reefs subsequently provided suitable sites for ore deposition from solutions derived from near-shore evaporites and off-shore marine shales.

(iii) Before the Earth's atmosphere became rich in oxygen, iron liberated by weathering could have been transported as $Fe^{2+}(aq)$ ions before precipitation as iron(III) oxides in shallow seas extending over large areas of early continental crust, which now form stable cratons.

(iv) High-temperature hydrothermal vein deposits and porphyry ores occur within and around the roof zones of granitic plutons. Over long periods of time, granites tend to be uplifted due to their buoyancy and are eroded to a great depth, where they are largely unmineralized.

(v) Oxygenation of the Earth's atmosphere occurred during the period 1 700–2 500 Ma ago. Conditions at the Earth's surface became more oxidizing; this enabled uraninite to be broken down by weathering and oxidation, and allowed uranium(VI), in the form of the complex ion UO_2^{2+}, to enter solution.

Distribution of ore deposits

In the geological record there is a tendency for ore deposits of a similar kind to be grouped within a particular geographic region, often known as a **metallogenic province**.

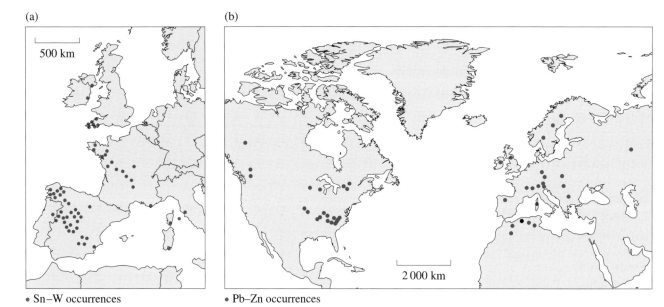

(a)

500 km

(b)

2 000 km

• Sn–W occurrences   • Pb–Zn occurrences

For example, the granites of Cornwall are famous for their associated hydro-thermal ores of tin and copper (along with lesser amounts of tungsten), as are other granites of similar age elsewhere in Europe. Together, they form well-defined belts, which are, in effect, metallogenic provinces (Figure 77a). Other examples of metallogenic provinces include iron ore formations in Russia and Ukraine (Figure 76), and hydrothermal lead–zinc deposits in the Carboniferous limestones of Europe and North America (Figure 77b).

Metal ore deposits grouped in this way and formed roughly at *the same time* often originate from major tectonic processes at plate boundaries. Consequently, they tend to occur on a huge scale, extending for hundreds or even thousands of kilometres. The Cornish tin deposits, for example, are thought to have formed after two continental masses came together about 295 Ma ago to form a zone of thickened crust, which melted at depth to form granites that occur not just in south-west England but over much of western Europe (Figure 77a).

Another reason for regional localization of ore deposits is **inheritance**, which involves the presence of anomalously high concentrations of metals in regions of continental crust or underlying mantle. Such concentrations provide sources for mineral deposit formation over long periods. In other words, where a metal anomaly has been established, it is *reworked* by igneous, hydrothermal and sedimentary processes of the rock cycle, so that new deposits of the same metal keep appearing in the *same region*, but at *different times*. An excellent example is featured in Figure 78, which shows one of the world's major nickel provinces in central Canada. This province contains nickel deposits of four different ages. The oldest deposits are associated with belts of ancient metamorphic rocks of basalt and peridotite composition (called 'greenstone belts'); the next are located around zones of faulting (Thompson); then come the famous Sudbury deposits, followed by a further set of deposits (Duluth), both of which are associated with large gabbroic intrusions. The time span between the oldest and youngest of these deposits (Figure 78) is 1 500 Ma, about one-third of Earth history.

Figure 77 Distribution of (a) tin deposits in western Europe, and (b) lead–zinc deposits in Europe and North America.

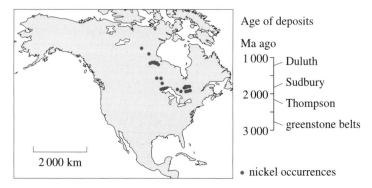

Age of deposits

Ma ago

1 000 — Duluth

Sudbury

2 000 — Thompson

3 000 — greenstone belts

2 000 km

• nickel occurrences

Figure 78 Distribution and age of nickel deposits in central Canada.

Question 40

Explain why similar ore deposits often occur in the same area.

5.4 Why study the formation of ore deposits?

At the end of the introduction (in Section 1.6), we posed questions that were intended to highlight the importance of studying the geology of ore deposits. It is of the utmost importance to the metals extraction industry to know about the global distribution, occurrence and abundance of ore deposits. Without that background knowledge, it would be difficult to find new deposits, to decide whether to invest in and plan the development of a particular deposit, to evaluate the future value of reserves, and to weigh current demands for metals and commercial profitability against conservation and environmental considerations. These are all aspects of the metals industry that will be examined in the second part of this Block.

If you can answer Question 41, you should be well prepared to tackle *Metals 2*.

Question 41

Use your knowledge of metal deposit formation to answer the following:

(a) In what tectonic setting would you look for molybdenum deposits, and why?

(b) With what association of rock types might you find lead–zinc deposits, and why?

(c) In what type of igneous intrusion might you find platinum deposits and why?

5.5 Summary of Section 5

1   The concentration of metals to produce ore deposits involves igneous, sedimentary and aqueous fractionation by natural physical and/or chemical processes in magmatic, sedimentary and hydrothermal systems. Most of these processes occur within the rock cycle. Many are driven by plate tectonic activity.

2   Mineral deposits linked to specific tectonic settings are:

- podiform chromites, Cyprus-type massive sulphides and metalliferous sediments, which *form* at constructive plate margins, but are *preserved* at former destructive plate margins;

- porphyry (copper and molybdenum) ore deposits and Kuroko-type massive sulphide deposits, which form at destructive plate margins;

- pegmatite and high-temperature hydrothermal vein deposits associated with granites, which form in collision settings at former destructive plate margins.

- sedimentary deposits, such as ironstones, and the limestone hosts of hydrothermal Pb–Zn deposits, which form in shallow sedimentary basins at stable continental margins.

- banded iron formations and stratiform igneous segregation deposits, which occur in ancient, relatively stable parts of continents, the cratons.

3   Many types of mineral deposit are restricted to particular geological settings. Links with particular geographic locations and geological ages are important for mineral exploration.

OPTIONAL FURTHER READING

Alexander, W., and Street, A. (1990) *Metals in the Service of Man*, Penguin. A classic book now into its ninth edition. A useful introduction to metallurgy and the diverse uses of metals.

Barnes, J. W. (1988) *Ores and Minerals: Introducing Economic Geology*, Open University Press. A useful account of mineral deposits in the broadest sense. Provides concise coverage of most types of ore deposit and other physical resources.

Blunden, J., and Reddish, A., eds (1991) *Energy, Resources and Environment*, Open University U206 text. Chapters 2 and 3 are relevant to Block 5.

Evans, A. M. (1993) *Ore Geology and Industrial Minerals: an Introduction*, Blackwell. A thorough and comprehensive account of mineral and ore deposit occurrence and formation.

Kellaway, G. A., ed. (1991) *Hot Springs of Bath*, Bath City Council. An authoritative account of the past use, and investigations into the source and composition of the thermal waters of the Bath area, providing an in-depth coverage.

Pellant, C. (1992) *Rocks and Minerals*, Eyewitness Handbook. Dorling Kindersley. Gives well-illustrated descriptions of all the minerals and many of the rocks mentioned in this Block.

OBJECTIVES

Now that you have completed Block 5 Part 1, you should be able to do the following:

1 Explain in your own words, and use correctly, the terms in the Glossary that relate to Block 5 Part 1.

2 Account for the extent to which metals are used in terms of (i) their properties, which influence demand, and (ii) their availability, which influences supply, and how both of these factors affect prices.

3 Explain:
 (a) why metals are extracted from ore minerals contained in ore deposits;
 (b) the importance of natural concentration processes in the formation of ore deposits;
 (c) the meanings of the terms 'ore mineral', 'ore', 'grade', 'reserves' and 'cut-off grade'.

4 Recognize the more important ore minerals, and explain why most metals form either oxides or sulphides, and how impurities can be valuable as by-products.

5 Describe the characteristics of dispersed and confined deposits.

6 Explain how metals in the natural environment can be both beneficial and harmful to living organisms.

7 Discuss the extent to which the exploitation of ore deposits can be sustained and how resources can be conserved.

8 Account for ore deposit formation in terms of Sources of metals, Agents of transportation, sites and conditions of Deposition, and Energy to drive a mineralizing system.

9 Explain the magmatic concentration processes that form cumulate ore deposits, pegmatite ores and porphyry ore deposits, and explain why these deposits are associated with gabbroic, granitic and granodioritic igneous rocks, respectively.

10 Describe the form and occurrence of layered chromite and sulphide deposits, pegmatite deposits rich in incompatible elements, and copper and molybdenum porphyry deposits.

11 Explain the involvement of both physical and chemical processes in concentrating elements and ore minerals at the surface of the Earth to form ore deposits.

12 Describe the form and occurrence of residual deposits, secondary enrichment deposits, bedded iron ores, manganese nodules and placer deposits.

13 Describe the workings of a hydrothermal system in the context of SPADE.

14 Explain the various factors that favour the concentration of elements to form ore deposits in a hydrothermal system.

15 Describe the form and occurrence of hydrothermal deposits precipitated from hot aqueous fluids that: rise towards the land surface; emerge onto the sea floor; circulate around granitic intrusions; migrate into limestones from shales compacting in sedimentary basins.

16 Discuss relationships between ore-forming processes and the rock cycle.

17 Account for the occurrence of ore deposits in their global setting and the role of plate tectonic processes in their formation.

18 Explain how studying the distribution, occurrence and character of ore deposits may assist in exploration, exploitation and management of metal resources.

ANSWERS TO QUESTIONS

Question 1

(a) The filament of a lightbulb needs to reach a high temperature ($\approx 2\,700\,°C$) to emit light; tungsten has a very high melting temperature ($3\,410\,°C$).

(b) Glass thermometers normally contain liquids, which expand and contract with changing temperature much more than solids. Mercury is the only metal with low enough melting temperature ($-39\,°C$) to be a liquid at normal temperatures. Its metallic appearance — that is, its colour, reflectivity and opacity — make it clear to see.

(c) Aircraft construction requires light but strong materials. Aluminium ($2.7\,\text{t m}^{-3}$) has a lower density than titanium ($4.5\,\text{t m}^{-3}$), but it is not as strong as titanium and melts at a much lower temperature ($659\,°C$). Hence titanium is particularly useful in high-speed aircraft, where frictional heating causes the aircraft frame to reach a high temperature.

(d) Power cables need to conduct electricity well and to be light, so that large spans can be supported. Aluminium is much lighter (by a factor of more than 3) than copper, the best conductor of the common metals, and, even though an aluminium cable is slightly less conductive than a copper cable of the same thickness, weight for weight it is more conductive (Block 1). It is also cheaper, weight for weight, than copper. However, in practice a steel core is used to increase the strength of power cables.

Question 2

(a) and (b)   The missing entries in Table 2 are shown in colour in Table 22.

Table 22 (completed Table 2)   Properties typically required of metals in common applications; the suitable metals suggested also take price into account

Application examples	Tensile strength	Workability	Hardness	Corrosion resistance	Appearance	Suitable metal
structures (bridges)	✓	✓		✓		Fe
transport (car chassis)	✓	✓		✓		Fe
tools (spanner)	✓		✓	✓	✓	Fe
electrical components (wire)	✓	✓		✓		Cu
cooling systems (car radiator)		✓		✓		Cu
containers (can)		✓		✓	✓	Al, (Fe)
fluid transport (pipe)	✓	✓		✓		Cu, Fe
fastenings (screws)	✓	✓		✓		Fe
weaponry (guns)	✓		✓	✓		Fe
ornamentation (jewellery)		✓		✓	✓	Au
money (coins)		✓		✓	✓	Cu, Ni

(c) (i) Thermal conductivity is important in cooling systems;
(ii) electrical conductivity is important in electrical components.

(d) Workability and corrosion resistance are important in most applications.

Question 3

(a) The raw materials of cupro-nickel cost much less than silver.

(b) Stainless steel does not rust and is hard enough to keep a sharp edge. Both these properties are important factors for the long-term durability of cutting equipment.

(c) Solder melts at a lower temperature (203 °C) than either pure tin (232 °C) or pure lead (328 °C), and lead is much cheaper than tin.

(d) Many rocks are very difficult to break, especially igneous and metamorphic rocks that contain quartz, which is harder than the steel used for knife blades, so a very hard metal is required for crushing. Manganese steel is used because it is a very hard alloy.

Question 4

(a) The notional value of iron mined = $\$5.02 \times 10^8 \times 205 = \$103 \times 10^9$.

The notional value of gold mined = $\$2\,250 \times 1.11 \times 10^7 = \$25 \times 10^9$.

(b) Notional value of metals (iron + manganese + chromium + nickel) used in steels = $\$(103 + 10.2 + 10.7 + 6.5) \times 10^9 = \$130.4 \times 10^9$.

Notional value of the major metals aluminium + copper + zinc = $\$(24.4 + 21.3 + 8.9) \times 10^9 = \$54.6 \times 10^9$.

Thus, the notional value of metals used in steel-making is about 2.5 times that of notable metals used in their own right, demonstrating the dominance of iron and steel in the metals markets.

Question 5

The structure of cassiterite could accommodate Fe^{3+}, Ti^{4+} and Nb^{5+} ions as substituted impurities, because they are of similar ionic radius (Figure 7) and their charges are the same as, or not very different from Sn^{4+}.

Question 6

Concentration factors are 375 for Zn, 91 for Ni, 67 for Cu, 2 000 for Sn, and 1 333 for Au.

Question 7

(a) The percentage of lead recycled = $2\,435 \times 100/5\,420 = 45\%$, which is the highest proportion of all the metals listed.

(b) A large proportion of lead is recycled because much of it is used in batteries, as protection for cables, and in building. All of these uses involve the metal itself rather than in a combined form. The largest proportion goes into batteries, which have a life of only a few years and are therefore recyclable on a fairly short time-scale. There is not much that can be done with a 'dead' battery, except to dump it or recycle it.

(c) Lead used as additives in petrol is dispersed with engine exhaust fumes into the atmosphere, into soils and into surface run-off, so it is imposs-ible to recycle, other than by natural processes over an extremely long time-scale.

Question 8

Veins are narrow sheets of crystalline rock, which form where minerals have precipitated in fluid pathways that are constricted to narrow channels such as joints or fractures. Low-porosity, brittle rocks, in which fractures open up during tectonic movements most commonly form suitable hosts. These include metamorphic, igneous and well-cemented sedimentary rocks.

Fluid pathways are more likely to be diffuse in soft, porous rocks, the kind that would make good aquifers or oil reservoirs. In these circumstances, dispersed deposits could result rather than hydrothermal veins.

Question 9

From peridotite to granite compositions:

(a)   FeO, Fe_2O_3 and MgO concentrations decrease;

(b) Na_2O and K_2O increase;

(c)   silica increases.

Question 10

The completed Table 10 is shown as Table 23. The missing concentration factors and rock types are shown in colour.

Table 23 (completed Table 10)   Typical abundances of some trace elements in a range of common intrusive igneous rocks

Trace metals	Peridotite/ ppm	Gabbro/ ppm	Diorite/ ppm	Granite/ ppm	Igneous rock type with greatest abundance	Average minimum exploitable grade/ppm	Minimum concentration factor
chromium, Cr	2 000	200	30	10	peridotite	300 000	150
copper, Cu	20	70	50	10	gabbro	5 000	71
lithium, Li	0.5	10	22	40	granite	20 000	500
nickel, Ni	2 000	130	30	5	peridotite	10 000	5
niobium, Nb	5	15	25	40	granite	1 000	25
platinum, Pt	0.05	0.01	0.005	0.001	peridotite	5	100
tantalum, Ta	0.25	0.75	1.5	2.5	granite	500	200
tin, Sn	0.5	1.5	2	3.5	granite	5 000	1 430
titanium, Ti	5	10 000	5 000	1 000	gabbro	30 000	3
tungsten, W	0.5	1.0	1.5	2.0	granite	5 000	2 500
uranium, U	0.005	1	2	3.5	granite	350	100
vanadium, V	60	400	100	30	gabbro	20 000	50

Question 11

(a) The missing words are shown below in colour.

The ore minerals in both the chromite-rich and PGE-rich layers are dense and form sequences of thin layers over a wide area. They formed by gravity settling and the repeated injection of magma pulses during crystallization of the intrusion. The chromite layers contain minerals that crystallized from the magma, whereas the Merensky Reef contains sulphide minerals that originally separated as an immiscible melt, scavenged the more electronegative metals from the magma and collected some chromite crystals on settling.

(b) PGE reserves of 60 000 t represent only 80% of the total PGE. There would be

$$60\,000 \times \frac{100}{80} = 75\,000\,t$$

contained in $1\,500 \times 10^9\,t$ of magma. This represents an average (initial) concentration of:

$75 \times 10^9\,g$ PGE in $1\,500 \times 10^9\,t$ of magma, or

$$\frac{75 \times 10^9}{1\,500 \times 10^9} = 0.05\,g\,t^{-1} \quad \text{in the undifferentiated magma.}$$

The concentration factor required to produce an ore grade of $10\,g\,t^{-1}$ is therefore $10/0.05 = 200$ times.

Question 12

The metals that appear in Table 11 and Figure 7 are: Be, Cs, Li, Ta, Sn, W and U.

Comparing the radii of the ions of these metals with those of the major metals in order of increasing ionic charge:

Ionic charge +1: lithium has a far smaller ionic radius than sodium; caesium has a far larger ionic radius than either sodium or potassium.

Ionic charge +2: beryllium has a much smaller ionic radius than iron(II) or magnesium.

Higher ionic charges: tantalum, tin, tungsten and uranium all have ionic charges greater than any of the major elements.

The implication of these comparisons follows from the discussion in Section 2.1.1. These metals have ionic charges and radii that differ from the major elements and therefore they are *incompatible* in the structures of common rock-forming minerals.

Question 13

In these circumstances, the enrichment of lithium is equivalent to that shown for water, which is from 0.2 to 8.0%, an enrichment of 40 times. With an initial concentration of 10 ppm, the final concentration of lithium should be 400 ppm.

Question 14

(a) (i) At 1980s yearly extraction rates, 15 Mt ore yields:

$15\,000\,000 \times 0.000\,26 = 3\,900$ t uranium metal

With reserves of 120 000 t of uranium, the lifetime of the deposit would be:

$120\,000/3\,900 = 30.8$ years.

(ii) Extraction of only 2.5 Mt y^{-1} in the early 1990s is one-sixth of that rate. On that basis the lifetime of Rössing would be six times as long — i.e. ≈ 180 years.

(b) The future of the nuclear power industry is very uncertain (Block 4 Part 2). As this industry is the main consumer of uranium, the prosperity and lifetime of the Rössing mine is also very uncertain.

Question 15

(i) Hinder. Porphyry ore deposits depend on high levels of magmatic water to concentrate and scavenge metals, and to fracture rocks when the water boils on rising to a high level in the crust.

(ii) Hinder. At deep levels in the crust, under high pressure, water is more soluble in magma and will neither separate nor boil. Separation and boiling of magmatic water are essential factors in the formation of a porphyry ore deposit.

(iii) Favour. The fluids that form porphyry ore deposits derive most of their Cu, Mo and Sn from the magma. If the proportions of these elements in the magma are relatively high, it is more likely that the grade of the resulting deposit will be high.

(iv) Hinder. If the magma erupts, aqueous fluids will be lost to the atmosphere and not be available to form a porphyry deposit within the crust.

(v) Favour. Crystallization of anhydrous minerals such as feldspars increases the concentration of water in the magma.

Question 16

Magmatic water was the most important. Without magmatic water there would be no ore deposit at all. It was responsible for the initial concentration of copper on separation from magma during emplacement at shallow depth. More importantly, explosive boiling of magmatic water was responsible for the initial fracturing which created pathways for mineralizing fluids. Even though the highest-grade ores are not magmatic, but secondary deposits, and later, meteoric fluids overprint the earlier magmatic ones, it is the essential role of magmatic water that justifies the classification of porphyry ore deposits as igneous in origin.

Question 17

Peridotite is the more susceptible to weathering. It is composed of minerals that crystallize at high temperatures, mainly olivine, with pyroxene and a small proportion of plagioclase feldspar (Figure 21), all of which are particularly prone to decomposition by weathering (Figure 38). Granite may contain some plagioclase feldspar, but usually comprises mostly potassium feldspar, biotite mica and quartz, which form at low temperatures and are more resistant to weathering.

Question 18

(i)—(b)   Sand and gravel are sorted during physical transport and deposition.

(ii)—(a)   China clay is an insoluble product of chemical weathering.

(iii)—(c)   Evaporites are formed by precipitation of dissolved salts that are carried to the sea in solution.

Question 19

See Table 24. Of the rock compositions listed, granite has the highest proportion of alumina in the insoluble residue. It would appear to be the most likely to form a residual bauxite ore. However, granite also contains quartz, which is not as easily dissolved as is silica from decomposing minerals.

Table 24 (completed Table 12)   Estimation of alumina contents of insoluble weathering products for a range of igneous rock types; correct entries are shown in colour

	Peridotite	Gabbro	Diorite	Granite
% Al_2O_3 in rock	4.0	14.1	16.0	14.0
% Fe_2O_3 + TiO_2 in rock	14.1	15.0	9.1	2.9
total % of insoluble oxides (residue)	18.1	29.1	25.1	16.9
% Al_2O_3 content of insoluble residue	22.1	48.5	63.7	82.8

Question 20

Your list should have included the following: tropical climate; high and intermittent rainfall; the presence of volcanic ash of suitable composition for weathering to bauxite at the surface; suitable topography (hollows) to trap deposits; and suitable bedrock (limestone) to provide good drainage and minimize erosion of the bauxite.

Question 21

(a) (i)   After aluminium, iron is the most abundant metal in crustal rocks.

(ii)   Iron forms deposits of iron oxide and carbonate minerals, which are rich in iron and suitable for smelting.

(iii)   Iron ore deposits are well distributed around the world, often occurring at the Earth's surface and are extensive enough to be worked in bulk. They are sufficiently accessible and of sufficiently high grade to be worked with the minimum of effort and processing, which also helps to keep the price down.

(b)   Substitution of iron and steel by lightweight materials saves energy required in transportation and hence fuel resources.

Question 22

The missing concentration factors are 0.6 for Mg, 0.7 for K, 45.7 for Ni, 96.6 for Co, 34.7 for Cu and 9.8 for Zn. The enrichments by more than a factor of 10 (other than manganese) are in lead, cobalt, nickel and copper.

Question 23

Essentially, it is not economic to mine them. Only deposits that can be mined economically at the current time qualify as reserves; manganese nodules are a conditional resource. There are also problems concerning the present lack of an international agreement to control their exploitation and the potential environmental disruption which would have to be resolved before they could be regarded as reserves.

Question 24

Ilmenite, cassiterite, columbite, zircon and gold.

Ilmenite, cassiterite, columbite and zircon are dense and hard, and so are very likely candidates to be found in placer deposits. Although it is dense, bornite is a sulphide, rather like chalcopyrite, which breaks down in oxidizing waters, and is rather too soft to survive as large grains. Molybdenite and barite are soft and cleave too easily. Gold is also very soft, but, being a metal, it is malleable, so lumps and flakes bend and distort, but do not break up easily. Its very high density and chemical inertness mean that gold is the ideal placer mineral. Panning for gold must be the one form of mineral prospecting that everyone knows about! It was the classic means for recovering gold in the 1849 'Gold Rush' to California (as you will see in Video Band 14: *Gold rush in the 1990s*).

Question 25

The heavy minerals were *Sourced* from the crystalline rocks of the Australian interior. Surface water was the *Agent* through which chemical weathering and erosion liberated heavy minerals and transported them via eastward-flowing rivers to the coast. Waves driven by south-easterly winds transported mineral grains along the shore to be *Deposited* on a beach, where concentration processes involved agitation of beach sands by wave action, which sorted and winnowed the grains, separating heavy minerals from the lighter sand grains. Winnowing by strong winds also removed the lighter sand grains. *Energy* was provided by the Sun's heat to evaporate water and form rain clouds, and by gravity — acting first on rainwater, which liberated grains by weathering and then on surface water run-off to transport them. Wind energy, derived from the Earth's rotation and the Sun's heat, drives the waves, which, together with gravity, acts on the grains to sort them.

Question 26

(i)   No. At the base of a sedimentary pile, compaction closes down available space. Formation water containing dissolved metal ions is expelled, outwards and upwards. It is more likely for the base of a sediment pile to be a source of metals rather than a site of deposition. Ore deposits generally form where space opens up, hydrothermal fluids are cooling, or gases are being released.

(ii)   Yes. A granite pluton can supply heat to drive a convecting hydrothermal system. Hydrothermal fluids would cool on passing through fractures in the overlying rocks. Given a fertile source of metals, this location would be suitable for an ore deposit to form.

(iii) Yes. Limestone is susceptible to solution along joints and fractures, which leads to the formation of cavities, or even caverns making ideal sites for ore deposition.

Question 27

(a) Na, Ca and K. They are between 5 and 70 times more concentrated in the Salton Sea brine than in seawater.

(b) Fe, Mn, Cu, Pb, Zn, Ba, Rb, Li and Ag are enriched in the Salton Sea brine more than 1 000 times above their concentration in seawater.

(c) The Salton Sea brine is an extremely saline solution, dominated by Na^+, Ca^{2+}, K^+ and Cl^- ions. It is very rich in trace metals, and is slightly acidic (pH 6).

(d) The Broadlands fluid is only about a tenth as saline as seawater, but is richer than seawater in some trace metals (Rb, Li) It is also slightly more alkaline than seawater (pH 8.6).

(e) Salton Sea fluids clearly contain much higher concentrations of dissolved salts, which would be liable to precipitate and fur up pipework, thereby causing a constant maintenance problem. Hence the more dilute Broadlands fluids would be better suited to supply a geothermal plant.

Question 28

Many metals that form *insoluble* sulphides form *soluble* complex ions with the HS^- ion. These ions provide a means of transporting metals and sulphur in the same solution, ultimately to be deposited as sulphides when the complex breaks down, whereas they *could not* be transported together as metal cations and S^{2-} anions.

Question 29

Hydrothermal systems are the link because they are needed both for the formation of hydrothermal ore deposits and as the means for providing the hot steam and water required for a geothermal power station.

(a) In regions where hot rocks occur near the surface, hydrothermal fluids rise along faults and fractures. Hydrothermal fluids may react with minerals in rocks through which they pass, taking some elements — including trace metals — into solution. During their passage to the surface, these constituents may be precipitated as ore minerals. If the system is maintained for long enough and the supply of metals is large enough, an ore deposit may be formed.

(b) If large volumes of hydrothermal fluid occur in the rocks of geothermally active regions, drilling directly into a deep aquifer allows steam and hot water under pressure to rise rapidly to the surface. Underground supplies are replenished by groundwater percolation through hot rock. The heat energy can be harnessed to drive turbines and generate electricity.

Question 30

(b) and (g) are incorrect:

(b) prospectors worked progressively *upstream*;

(g) during the 1980s it became economic to mine *low*-grade deposits in Nevada.

Question 31

(a) They were panning for gold in alluvial placer deposits, which contained accumulations of dense gold particles in river gravels. The miners panned upstream looking for the source of the gold in hydrothermal veins ('the mother lode').

(b) The early miners could only prospect for vein deposits in the hills (the Ranges) where there was rock at the surface. Mineral deposits in the flat-floored valleys (the Basins), where faulting and hot spring activity had occurred, were concealed under many metres of sediment and alluvium, which could not possibly be dug out with hand tools.

(c) The gold in these low-grade ores is so fine (grain size $<50\,\mu m$) that it would not have been visible in their pans.

Question 32

Aspects of SPADE	Applicability to the ore deposits of Cyprus
Source: of ore constituents	metals scavenged from basaltic crust; sulphur mainly from SO_4^{2-} in seawater
Pathways: for fluid circulation	fractures in ocean floor, spaces between basalt pillows
Agent: water supply	seawater
Deposition: causes	cooling and changes in solution chemistry when hot, metal-rich hydrothermal fluids mix with cool seawater
Deposition: site	on ocean floor for massive ore; fractures in ocean floor for stockwork
Energy: heat source	heat from emplacement of magma in oceanic crust convects seawater in overlying rocks

Question 33

(a) Galena and sphalerite.

(b) 2–3% Pb; 5–6% Zn.

(c) Miners on the way to the Yukon and the Klondike area, where gold had been discovered, found that Indians used the heavy mineral, galena, to weight their fishing nets. They located sources of the galena, but found it contained little silver and so were not interested at the time.

Question 34

(a) 'Preparing the ground' means making space for mineralizing solutions and ore mineral deposition.

(b) Dissolution of limestones by acidic groundwater and extensive dolomitization of the limestone (alteration of calcium carbonate to calcium–magnesium carbonate) by magnesium-rich solutions. These processes produced numerous spaces through which ore-bearing fluids could pass.

(c) (i) Dissolution of limestone along vertical joints led to cylindrical collapse structures.

(ii) Dissolution of limestone along horizontal joints led to tabular collapse structures with more irregular shapes.

Question 35

Statement (e) is incorrect. The remoteness of Pine Point *greatly influenced* the time lag between proving the deposit and its exploitation. It meant building 650 km of railway, which was only started in 1962 after protracted negotiations with the Canadian Government.

Question 36

Sources   The lead and zinc could have come from one or more of the following sources: the marine shales (the most likely source); the Precambrian rocks, from which fluids travelled up along the main fault beneath the reef; the evaporites; or even the limestones, from which small amounts of metals were released during their dolomitization. Sulphur probably came from the evaporites as the sulphate ion, SO_4^{2-}.

Pathways   The dissolution of limestone along joints and bedding planes created pathways for metal-rich solutions that were either draining from, or being squeezed out of, the shales and the evaporites.

Agents   The agents that transported the essential components of the ore-forming process were probably:

(i) formation water containing hydrocarbons from the shales (this was originally seawater trapped in pores, along with decaying organic material);

(ii) brines rich in dissolved salts that originated as groundwater percolating through the evaporites.

Lead and zinc were most likely to have been transported as organic compounds associated with the hydrocarbons, and sulphur as sulphate ions.

Deposition   Spaces in the limestone were formed when:

(i) dissolution of limestone occurred during a period of uplift, when it was exposed to surface weathering, giving solution features, such as caves and sub-surface channelways;

(ii) magnesium-bearing solutions from evaporite basins altered some of the calcium carbonate of the reef limestone to dolomite, leaving cavities.

Caving-in and roof collapse produced a jumbled mass of limestone with abundant spaces in which metal-bearing solutions could deposit ore minerals (Figure 53c).

The insoluble sulphide ore minerals were probably formed when reducing solutions containing hydrocarbons mixed with oxidizing solutions containing sulphate ions. Reaction between hydrocarbons and sulphate ions would have produced hydrogen sulphide, and contact with lead and zinc ions in the metalliferous brines would have immediately precipitated the sulphide ore minerals.

Energy   This is harder to ascertain. Compaction under gravity at the base of the sedimentary pile would have expelled water into permeable rocks where pressure of burial was not so great. Although fluid temperatures were not very high, geothermal heat may have aided the convection of fluids.

Question 37

See Table 25.

Table 25   (completed Table 19) SPADE summary of the formation of the Pine Point and Cornish ore deposits

Location: metal ores	*Source* of ore constituents	Source of water *agent*	*Pathways* for fluid circulation	Cause of ore *deposition*	Site of ore *deposition*	Source of heat *energy*
Pine Point: Pb, Zn	shales, evaporites	meteoric and formation water	joints, fractures and solution cavities	reaction with limestone and cooling	cavities in limestone	normal geothermal heating
Cornwall: Sn, W, Cu, Zn, Pb	sedimentary rocks, volcanic rocks, granite	meteoric, formation and magmatic waters	joints and fractures	cooling and reaction with wall rocks	large fractures	emplacement of granite

Question 38

(i), (iv) and (v) are formed in a specific plate tectonic environment; (ii), (iii) and (vi) are non-specific.

(i) Porphyry copper deposits are specific to volcanic arcs overlying subduction zones.

(iv) Massive sulphide deposits *form* at sites of submarine oceanic volcanism, usually at mid-ocean ridges or volcanic island arcs, but *occur* as *ore deposits* at sites of former destructive plate margins.

(v) Hot spring deposits occur at sites of land-based volcanism, especially above subduction zones.

(ii) Secondary enrichment deposits are non-specific, although they are an important feature of many porphyry ore deposits (see (i) above); secondary enrichment can affect many types of sulphide mineral deposit.

Neither (iii) placer deposits nor (vi) residual deposits are specific to any plate tectonic setting.

Question 39

(a)—(iii), (b)—(ii), (c)—(iv), (d)—(i), (e)—(v). For more information about the kinds of deposit referred to, see Section 3.3.1 (for part a), Section 4.3.1 (for part b), Sections 2.4 and 4.3.2 (for part c), Section 3.2.1 (for part d) and Section 3.4 (for part e).

Question 40

The formation of many ore deposits is related to major tectonic features of the Earth, which are developed on a large scale, thus creating extensive regions where *similar types* of deposit formed at a *similar time*. The reworking of regional concentrations of a metal tends to produce spatially related deposits at *different times*, due to inheritance.

Question 41

(a) Molybdenum ores mainly occur in porphyry deposits, which are found in volcanic arcs at destructive plate margins above subduction zones. Porphyry deposits form where wet magmas are emplaced at a high level in the crust, and explosively release watery fluids rich in soluble metal ions. Molybdenite may be deposited as these fluids escape through fractures and react with minerals in the surrounding rocks.

(b) Lead–zinc deposits often occur in limestones, where joints and solution cavities provide pathways for fluids as well as space for ore mineral deposition. Reaction between limestone and hydrothermal fluids cause chemical changes which favour precipitation of sulphide minerals. Black shales provide a source from which metal-rich formation waters can be expelled on burial. Soluble minerals from evaporites dissolve in percolating groundwater to provide highly saline brines of a quite different character from those of the shale formation waters. Intermingling of the two types of water may cause precipitation of lead and zinc sulphide ore minerals.

(c) Layered gabbroic intrusions are of a suitable composition and provide suitable conditions for the formation of crystal cumulates and, if rich enough in sulphide, immiscible sulphide melts. These sulphide melts may scavenge the more electronegative metals, such as platinum, to produce platinum deposits.

ANSWERS TO ACTIVITIES

Activity 1

(a) (i)   In the writer's home, the first five items in which iron was detected were: a central heating radiator, the casing of a microwave oven, a kitchen knife, a door bolt, and a coat-hanger. The sink was made of stainless steel but curiously turned out to be non-magnetic austenitic steel.

(ii)   The first four aluminium items found were a saucepan, a drink can, a double-glazing window-frame, and kitchen foil.

(iii) Copper was visible in a loudspeaker cable, in water pipes, and in 2p and 1p coins. The most extensive use of copper around the home is in electrical wiring and the windings of electric motors and transformers, where the copper is normally protected by insulation and is therefore out of sight. Copper also tends to be used for hot water tanks, in central heating pipes and other indoor water pipes. Once copper was more readily available than stainless steel or aluminium; these materials have substituted for copper in kettles and saucepans because they are now made far more cheaply.

(b)   The three most important properties are likely to be:
  • for iron: strength, workability and cheapness;
  • for aluminium: lightness, workability and corrosion resistance;
  • for copper: electrical and thermal conductivity, and workability.

Copper would have been inappropriate for the bulky central heating radiator because of its high price compared with iron (Table 1). Iron would be inappropriate for the loudspeaker lead because it is a poor conductor of electricity compared with copper (Table 1).

Activity 2

(a) Your completed version of Figure 7 should be as shown in Figure 79.

(i) Na^+ and K^+ have the same ionic charge, but different ionic radii, whereas Na^+ and Ca^{2+} have different charges but similar ionic radii.

(ii) Mg^{2+} and Fe^{2+} have the same charges and similar ionic radii; the Fe^{3+} ion has a smaller ionic radius than the Fe^{2+} ion.

(iii) Both Rb^+ and Ba^{2+} have similar radii to K^+, so are more likely to substitute for it than they are for Na^+.

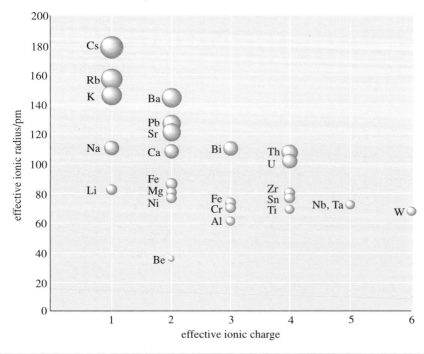

Figure 79 (completed Figure 7)   Plot of effective ionic charge against effective ionic radius for selected metals. Elements with similar ionic radius and the same ionic charge are more likely to substitute for each other in minerals.

(b) The more highly charged ions have smaller ionic radii. A greater ionic charge means there is a greater attraction for the electrons surrounding the nucleus; hence the size of the ion is smaller.

(c) Nickel is more likely to substitute for iron in pyrrhotite than for lead in galena because the size of the nickel ion is similar to that of iron but much smaller than that of lead.

Activity 3

(a) Reserves of metal in the dispersed deposit for a cut-off grade of 0.6% are 2.0 Mt copper, and for a cut-off grade of 0.4%, 4.0 Mt copper.

(b) With increasing *size* of the ore body in Figure 8a the average grade *decreases*, but the corresponding amount of ore, and the reserves of metal it contains, both *increase*.

(c) At a cut-off grade of 0.4% Cu, the ore body would then contain 800 Mt of ore at an average grade of 0.5% — that is, $800 \times 0.005 = 4$ Mt of copper — a reserve four times greater than for a cut-off of 0.8%. However, it would be necessary to mine 800 Mt of ore — sixteen times as much.

At a cut-off grade of 0.4% Cu there would be 796 Mt of waste, instead of only 49 Mt of waste at a cut-off grade of 0.8%. These estimates of waste assume that copper can be extracted as the metal. Usually it will be extracted as an ore mineral concentrate, and amounts of waste will be less.

(d) Reserves of metal in the confined deposit for a cut-off grade of 3% are 0.01 Mt copper, for a cut-off grade of 2% are 0.02 Mt copper, and for a cut-off grade of 1%, 0.022 Mt copper.

(e) Your completed version of Figure 9a should be as shown in Figure 80a.

(f) Your completed version of Figure 9b should be as shown in Figure 80b.

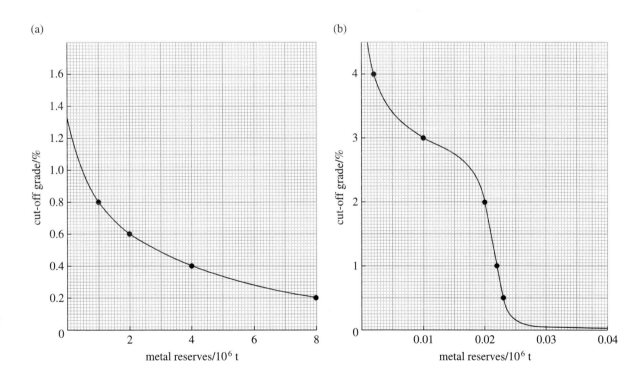

Figure 80 Completed grade–tonnage graphs for the (a) dispersed and (b) confined deposits featured in Figure 9a and 9b.

Activity 4

The completed and corrected form of Table 21 is shown in Table 26. Items inserted or corrected are shown in colour.

Table 26 (completed Table 21)   Summary of ore deposit formation

Deposit type	Geological environment	Concentration processes	Agent	Typical metals
magmatic segregation	layers in gabbroic intrusions	density settling of mineral grains and blobs of melt	basaltic magma (sulphide/oxide melt)	Cr, Ni, Cu, PGEs, Ti
pegmatite	roof zones of granitic intrusions	melt remaining after fractional crystallization	water-saturated granitic magma	Li, U, Ta, Cs, Be, Nb
porphyry	shallow porphyry intrusions in volcanic arcs	separation of aqueous fluid from magma, explosive fracturing, mixing with groundwater, reaction with host rocks and cooling	magmatic aqueous fluid (early); meteoric fluid (later)	Cu, Mo, (Sn)
residual	surface, tropical areas	residue left after weathering and removal of soluble ions	meteoric surface water	Al, Fe, Ni, Co, Au
secondary enrichment	near-surface, mineralized deposits	leaching and deposition	meteoric groundwater	Cu, Ag
bedded iron ore	submarine, shallow seas	sedimentary precipitation	seawater	Fe
manganese nodules	submarine, deep ocean	sedimentary precipitation	seawater	(Mn, Fe, Ni, Co, Cu, Zn)*
placer	rivers/coasts	sedimentary sorting	surface water	Sn, Ti, Au
hot spring-related	near-surface, land-based, hydrothermally active regions	hydrothermal precipitation, cooling fluids	mainly meteoric water	Au, Ag, Hg
massive sulphide	submarine, hydrothermally active regions	hydrothermal precipitation, cooling fluids	mainly seawater	Cu, Zn, Pb
sedimentary basin	sedimentary pile with shales, limestones and evaporites	hydrothermal precipitation, mixing fluids, host rock reaction	mainly formation and meteoric waters	Pb, Zn
granite intrusion-related	granite intruded into sedimentary pile	hydrothermal precipitation, cooling fluids	formation, meteoric and magmatic waters	Sn, W, Cu, Zn, Pb

* These metals do not form ore deposits of this kind at present.

ACKNOWLEDGEMENTS

The author would like to thank the Block Assessor, Dr A. M. Evans, for helpful comments and suggestions, and for information on the Kidd Creek deposit; Dr Andy Tindle, consultant on pegmatites; Dr Peter Abrahams, consultant on geology and health; and Cominco Ltd., for information on the current status of Pine Point.

Grateful acknowledgement is made to the following sources for permission to reproduce material in this Block:

Cover: Satellite composite view of Earth, copyright © 1990 Tom Van Sant/ The GeoSphere® Project, Santa Monica, California, with assistance from NOAA, NASA, EYES ON EARTH, technical direction Lloyd Van Warren, source data derived from NOAA/TIROS-N Series Satellites; all rights reserved; *Figure 1a*: Andy Tindle; *Figure 1b*: Adelheid Raqué-Nuttall; *Figure 24d*: Sir G. M. Brown and L. R. Wager *Layered Igneous Rocks*, Oliver & Boyd (1967); *Figure 27*: U.S. Geological Survey Photographic Library; *Figure 28*: P. Černý, 'Rare-element granite pegmatites. Part 1: Anatomy and internal evolution of pegmatite deposits', *Geoscience Canada*, **18** (2), p. 54 (1991); *Figure 30a* Chris Hawkesworth; *Figure 30b*: J. Berning, R. Cooke, S. A. Hiemstra and U. Hoffman, 'The Rössing uranium deposit, South West Africa', *Economic Geology*, **71** (1976), by permission of Economic Geologist Publishing Company; *Figure 31*: reproduced by courtesy of Kennecott Exploration Inc; *Figure 32b*: J. M. Guilbert and C. F. Park, *The Geology of Ore Deposits*, Freeman, New York (1986); *Figure 40*: E. de Chetelat, *Bulletin Soc. Geol. France*, **17** (1967), reproduced by permission of the Société Géologique de France; *Figure 41*: B. Mason, *Principles of Geochemistry*, Wiley (1966), reprinted by permission of John Wiley & Sons; *Figures 42, 51 and 65*: C. J. Dixon, *Atlas of Economic Mineral Deposits*, Chapman & Hall (1979); *Figure 44*: C. F. Park and R. A. MacDiarmid, *Ore Deposits*, Freeman (1970), copyright © 1970 by W. H. Freeman and Company; used with permission; *Figure 47a*: W. S. Broecker, *Chemical Oceanography*, Institute of Oceanographic Sciences (1974); *Figure 47b*: R. K. Sorem and R. H. Fewkes, *Manganese Nodules: Research Data and Methods of Investigation*, IFI-Plenum, New York and London (1979), by permission of R. K. Sorem; *Figure 48*: D. S. Cronan, *Underwater Minerals*, Academic Press Inc. (London) (1980); *Figure 52a, b and c*: The National Museum of Wales, Cardiff; *Figure 55*: J. N. Andrews, W. G. Burgess, W. M. Edmunds, R. L. F. Kay, D. J. Lee, 'The thermal springs of Bath', *Nature, Lond.* (1982), reprinted with permission from *Nature*, copyright © 1982 Macmillan Magazines Limited; *Figure 57*: E. Roedder, US Department of the Interior Geological Survey; *Figure 58b*: Richard Bevins; *Figure 58c and d*: Tony Waltham, Nottingham Trent University; *Figure 61*: Bramley Murton; *Figure 63*: M. S. Goldfarb, D. R. Convene, H. D. Holland and J. H. Edmond, *The Genesis of Hot Springs on the East Pacific Rise 21°1N*, Economic Geology Monographs (1983), pp. 184–197; *Figure 70a*: E. A. Edmonds, M. C. McKeown and W. Williams, *British Regional Geology: South-West England* (3rd edn, 1969), reproduced by permission of the Director, British Geological Survey. NERC; copyright reserved; *Figure 70b*: K. F. G. Hosking, *Trans. R. Geol. Soc. Cornwall*, **18** (1951), reproduced by permission of the Royal Geological Society of Cornwall; *Figure 76*: J. F. Dewey and B. Horsfield , 'Plate tectonics, orogeny and continental growth', *Nature, Lond.*, **225** (1970), reprinted with permission from *Nature*, copyright © 1970 Macmillan Magazines Limited; *Figure 77b*: R. L. Stanton, *Ore Petrology*, McGraw–Hill Inc. (1972).

Physical Resources and Environment